THE NEGLIGENT DOCTOR

OTHER BOOKS BY THE SAME AUTHOR

MEDICAL MALPRACTICE

RULES OF EVIDENCE IN NEGLIGENCE CASES

MEDICAL ASPECTS OF NEGLIGENCE CASES

THE
NEGLIGENT
DOCTOR

MEDICAL MALPRACTICE
in and out of Hospitals
and What Can Be Done About It

by

CHARLES KRAMER

CROWN PUBLISHERS, INC.   NEW YORK

To my wife,
without whose inspiration and guidance
this book
would never have seen the light of day

CONTENTS

PREFACE

Many of the medical malpractice cases presented in this book will undoubtedly shock you. Some of them may cause you to say, "Why, I know someone who had exactly the same experience"—though it probably was not brought to court.

These cases are startling and representative—and they are true. Though the names of the doctors, hospitals, and patients involved have been changed, the facts are authentic. In many instances, rather than attempting my own interpretation, I have presented the actual testimony so that you, the reader, can be a thirteenth juror, and thus draw your own conclusion.

I have not intended this book as an attack on the medical profession, for it has been my experience—garnered from many years as a practicing attorney specializing in medical negligence cases—that by and large doctors are a dedicated group of men who perform a great service to humanity. Some few, however, are not. And as the cases in this book unfold, you will see in some instances a story of carelessness, indifference, and even ignorance on the part of some doctors. This is a serious state of affairs—one that may affect your future or the life of someone near and dear to you.

My book, quite simply, has two basic objectives: to alert the victims of medical negligence, and to remind the medical profession that it has pledged itself to exert care, wisdom, and professionalism in its treatment of those who have entrusted their health and very life to its abilities.

—CHARLES KRAMER

THE NEGLIGENT DOCTOR

"Medicine is, of all the Arts, the most noble . . . but owing to the ignorance of those who practice it, and of those who, inconsiderately, form a judgment of them, it is at present far behind all the other arts. Their mistake appears to me to arise principally from this, that in the cities there is no punishment connected with the practice of medicine (and with it alone) except disgrace, and that does not hurt those who are familiar with it. Such persons are like the figures which are introduced in tragedies, for as they have the shape, the dress, and the personal appearance of an actor, but are not actors, so also physicians are many in title but very few in reality."

—HIPPOCRATES

I

DOCTOR, "FIRST, NO HARM"

*Why the medical profession should be held
accountable for their carelessness*

"It is reliably estimated," Dr.
Paul R. Hawley, Director of the American College of Surgeons, has said, "that *one-half* of the surgical operations in the United States are performed by doctors who are untrained or inadequately trained to undertake surgery."

Does the figure astound you? Does it call to mind some instances, within your own small circle of friends and relatives, of possible medical malpractice—in any of a score of fields—by a doctor, dentist, nurse, hospital, or medical assistant? Quite probably. The scope and gravity of the problem are undeniable. Violating fundamental principles of good treatment has become so alarmingly widespread that one responsible physician recently wrote in a medical periodical an article entitled "We Need More Malpractice Suits." He commented: "If patients brought malpractice suits against all guilty doctors—and against guilty doctors only—the courts would probably be flooded with *three times* the number of such suits now in litigation. . . . Though we all know about such abuses, too often we doctors keep our mouths shut."

No one likes to think that the doctor to whom one has entrusted his health—and very life—is incompetent; and it would be grossly wrong to encourage distrust where no grounds for distrust exist, to be an alarmist when no smoke is visible. But the evidence is undeniable: Medical negligence, with its ensuing damage to life and limb, does exist, and on a much broader scale than most people would believe. When it does occur, it is the right of the victim to seek, through the courts, fair and adequate compensation. By doing so, he can often minimize—to the degree that this can be done financially—the harm he has suffered. He will also be contributing to the growing demand for more adequate and careful medical practice.

But just how widespread is medical negligence? How great is the threat?

The famous Trussell report is an illuminating place to start. Published in 1962, it dealt with the treatment given to patients in 101 hospitals in New York. Its sad conclusion was that in those hospitals that were not affiliated with medical schools or were not accredited with the Joint Commission, "only one-third of the cases were considered to have received good or excellent care and 43 percent were judged to have received poor care."

The report went on to note that despite the large number of fine hospitals and the high proportion of well-trained physicians, inferior care often resulted from poor clinical judgment on the part of a certain number of attending physicians *who were neither adequately trained nor supervised*. It further stated, in a more specific reference, that one-third of the hysterectomies (removal of the uterus) that were performed were "unnecessary" and "that some question could be raised about the advisability of the operation in another ten percent of the cases." Because of its pointed, though valid, criticism of the treatment afforded the public, the Trussell report was itself the subject of severe attack from many branches of medicine, and, unfortunately, has rarely been heard of since.

More recently, the *New York Times* of March 10, 1967, reported that a New York legislator had paid a surprise visit to the Flower and Fifth Avenue Hospitals (a leading voluntary hospital in New York City) and found that the Emergency Room of this 400-bed institution (one of the five medical-college hospitals in the city) had no resuscitators, no respirators, no defibrillators, and no electrocardiagram machines (all these vital lifesaving instruments are available in the emergency rooms of each of the twenty-one municipal-owned hospitals). The legislator further found that only an *intern* was on duty, instead of a *resident physician*—as required even in city hospitals.

Is it any wonder, then, that so much medical malpractice, with its awesome toll of life and health, occurs?

In recent years there has been a definite increase in the number of lawsuits against doctors and hospitals because of negligence. Unfortunately, the medical profession has taken the attitude that most of these claims are unfounded, and it has exerted great efforts to resist them. There is an ironic short-sightedness in this. Since it is a cardinal rule of medicine to treat the "disease" rather than its "symptoms," it is precisely in the area of *prevention* of unnecessary human suffering and the tragic loss of human lives that the doctors should be directing their energies—not in diatribes against the lawsuit. Wise men have said, "It is better to light a single candle than to curse the darkness."

There is a basic principle of law that whenever you grant *immunity* from fault you breed *irresponsibility*. The value of the malpractice lawsuit is that in addition to remedying a wrong to a patient, it also keeps the doctors on their toes. Only by holding the medical profession accountable for their carelessness can we hope to have them reduce the errors of their ways. What is needed—and what, among other goals, this book seeks to promote—is a return to basics: namely, to the first principle of medicine, *Primum non nocere* (First, no harm to the patient). Therein lies the answer to malpractice cases.

But before we explore a representative group of such cases, it is necessary to establish pertinent criteria. How, after all, does a man recognize that he is a victim of medical negligence? How does he know if he has a valid case?

II

ARE YOU A VICTIM OF
MEDICAL NEGLIGENCE?*

*The basic tenets of the law governing
medical malpractice*

Charging a doctor with malpractice is a serious matter and should not be done without careful consideration of the facts and the medical literature pertaining to them. Your attorney knows this, and he has a duty not to proceed unless he is fully satisfied that malpractice has, in fact, occurred.

The doctor is not necessarily guilty of malpractice every time there is an adverse result. On the contrary, in many cases the doctor will have done everything humanly and medically possible to effect a cure. In others—and these are the ones with which we shall be concerned—the doctor has failed to exercise the requisite care, skill, and diligence. Malevolence is rarely the cause, but *professional negligence* is.

* A more thorough and technical approach to the material in this chapter may be found in my book *Medical Malpractice* (New York: Practicing Law Institute, 1965). That book—from which sections of this chapter have been adapted—was written primarily for the legal profession.

19

To be more precise, malpractice may be defined as "bad or unskillful practice on the part of a physician or surgeon [or dentist] resulting in injury to the patient"; or "the treatment by a surgeon or physician in a manner contrary to accepted rules and with injuries resulting to the patient."

There are three essential elements to any medical malpractice case:

1. a relationship of *physician* and *patient* actually existed;
2. the physician departed from some *duty* that he owed to the patient;
3. the departure was the *proximate* cause of the injury.

Let's carefully consider each of these crucial elements.

THE RELATIONSHIP OF PHYSICIAN AND PATIENT

This relationship is usually the result of a voluntary agreement between the patient and the physician. The *conduct* of the parties determines the relationship. Ordinarily very few formal words are exchanged, and even the matter of fee is often not discussed. Even if no fee is involved, this does not alter the relationship.

A doctor is under no duty to render his services to anyone, and is not liable for consequences of such a failure to treat unless he is connected with a governmental agency or a hospital that has a specific duty and obligation to the members of the general public.

The central doctor-and-patient relationship, which imposes a duty to use care, may arise when the services of the doctor have been obtained for the patient's benefit, even though the patient did not himself hire the doctor. The relationship may also be created by an agreement between the doctor and a third person who is not the patient.

Indeed, the relationship can arise merely from a *telephone conversation*. Not too long ago, a man who had had a heart attack came to the emergency room of a prominent hospital in the early hours of the morning. He was accompanied by his wife. The nurse in charge was told about the heart attack, and treatment was requested. But when the man mentioned that he was a member of the Health Insurance Plan, the nurse replied that the hospital could not take care of patients of that plan, but would try to get a HIP doctor. She telephoned the co-defendant, and explained the facts to him; then the heart-attack sufferer took the telephone and described his pains to the doctor. When the conversation ended, he informed the nurse that the doctor had told him to go home and to return when HIP was open. The man's wife again asked the nurse to get a doctor because this was an emergency, but the nurse refused and said that the patient would have to see his own doctor. The man returned to his apartment, and, while undressing, fell to the floor and died.

The doctor's version of the telephone conversation was that he offered to come to the emergency room *and examine* the heart-attack victim but that the latter had declined, stating that he felt better and would prefer to see another doctor.

The trial court dismissed the case on the grounds that there was no valid relationship between physician and patient, but the appellate court reversed the dismissal as to both the doctor and the hospital. It stated that the jury could have concluded that the doctor *"undertook to diagnose the ailments of the deceased* and could have decided whether he abandoned the patient, inadequately or improperly advised him or, conversely, made a proper diagnosis fully appropriate under the circumstances, or offered an examination which was rejected."

DUTY OWED BY PHYSICIAN TO PATIENT

The leading case of *Pike v. Honsinger* (1898), recognized throughout the country, succinctly expresses the obligation owed by a doctor to his patient. Since it is such a classic case, it is worth quoting at length.

The doctor must possess

> . . . that reasonable degree of learning and skill that is ordinarily possessed by physicians in *the locality where he practices*. . . .
>
> [He is] to use reasonable care and diligence in the exercise of his skill and the application of his learning to accomplish the purpose for which he was employed.
>
> [He should] use his best judgment in exercising his skill and applying his knowledge.
>
> . . . he is bound to keep abreast of the times.
>
> . . . a departure from approved methods in general use, if it injures the patient, will render him liable however good his intentions may have been.

However, the opinion goes on to say:

> The rule in relation to learning and skill does not require the surgeon to possess that extraordinary learning and skill which belongs only to a few men of rare endowments, but such as is possessed by the average member of the medical profession in good standing.
>
> . . . the rule of reasonable care and diligence does not require the exercise of the highest possible degree of care . . .

and

> it is not enough that there has been a less degree of care than some other medical men might have shown, or less than even he might have bestowed, but there must be a want of ordinary and reasonable care, leading to a bad result.
>
> . . . the rule requiring him to use his *best* judgment, does

not hold him liable for a *mere error of judgment*, provided he does what he thinks is best after careful examination.

[He] does not guarantee a good result, but he promises by implication to use the skill and learning of the average physician, to exercise reasonable care and to exert his best judgment in the effort to bring about a good result.

Since a doctor cannot be held liable for a *mere error of judgment* (providing he has made a careful examination), this is a common defense in malpractice cases. In one case, concerning a wrong diagnosis, it was held that a mistake in the interpretation of a spot X ray of the chest that was routinely taken of a hospital employee was an "error of judgment" for which the defendant was not liable. But in another, the court stated that where the X ray of the chest was *positive* and the defendant through its employee, the doctor, knew that the plaintiff had tuberculosis, it was negligent not to inform him of that fact; and even the plaintiff's wife, who contracted tuberculosis, had a cause of action.

The most frequent allegation of malpractice is that the doctor failed to use reasonable skill and diligence in the care and treatment of the plaintiff, and failed to use the accepted and proper methods. Rarely, if ever, has it been shown that the doctor did not possess the requisite skill or that he did not use his best judgment.

Where the doctor is a *specialist*, he is bound to exercise the degree of skill and knowledge that is ordinarily possessed by similar specialists, and not merely the degree of skill and knowledge of a general practitioner. On the other hand, a general practitioner who undertakes to treat a case that clearly lies within the field of a special branch of medicine will be held liable for failure to use skill equal to that of a specialist in that field.

Let's now consider some of the specific obligations of the doctor:

1. At the very outset it should be kept clearly in mind that "the physician is in a position of trust and confidence as regards his patient, and it is his duty to act with the utmost good faith toward the patient. *If he knows that he cannot accomplish a cure,* or that the treatment adopted will probably be of no benefit, it is his duty to advise his patient of these facts."

2. Even though a doctor performs his services gratuitously, he must still "exercise reasonable and ordinary care, skill and diligence."

3. The doctor must make a "skillful and careful diagnosis" of the patient's ailment," and must "inform himself by the proper tests and examinations of the condition of his patient to undergo a proposed treatment or operation."

4. The duty of exercising reasonable skill and diligence also includes "the giving of proper instructions to his patient in relation to conduct, exercise and the use of an injured limb."

Furthermore, when a doctor or hospital discovers that the patient has a condition that requires treatment, there is a duty to disclose this fact to the patient and to give him proper instructions in the use of any needed medication.

5. A physician cannot fail to give a patient *proper aftercare* treatment or *abandon* him without risking legal responsibility for any ill effects. In fact, the doctor is under a duty to give the patient all necessary care as long as the case requires attention, and an unwarranted lack of diligence in attending the patient renders the physician liable for malpractice.

The duty of a doctor to call on his patient does not diminish merely because he is receiving care in a reputable hospital and is being seen by other doctors.

6. "The complaints, observations and remonstrances of a patient must be heeded by the physician to a reasonable extent."

7. A doctor may be liable for malpractice if, in rendering treatment to which the plaintiff consents, he *fails to make a frank disclosure to plaintiff of the risk involved in the procedure.*

In a pioneering case on this subject, *Natanson v. Kline*, plaintiff's left breast had been removed because of cancer. The surgeon had recommended to the plaintiff that she have the head radiologist of the hospital give her therapy to the site of the mastectomy. Plaintiff claimed she was given a series of cobalt radiation treatments in such a negligent manner that the skin, flesh, and muscles beneath her left arm sloughed away and the ribs on her left side were burned. She sued the radiologist and the hospital. The case was submitted to the jury on the usual grounds of negligence, and the jury found for the defendants.

In reversing the judgment for defendant and ordering a new trial, the appellate court stated:

> Anglo-American law starts with the premise of thorough-going self-determination. It follows that each man is considered to be master of his own body, and he may, if he is of sound mind, expressly prohibit the performance of life-saving surgery, or other medical treatment. . . .
>
> We think, upon all the facts and circumstances here presented, Dr. Kline was obliged to make a reasonable disclosure to the appellant of the nature and probable consequences of the suggested or recommended cobalt irradiation treatment and he was also obliged to make a reasonable disclosure of the dangers within his knowledge which were incident to, or possible in, the treatment he proposed to administer. . . .

The court then went on to say:

> On retrial of this case, the first issue for the jury to determine would be whether the administration of cobalt irradiation treatment was given with the *informed* consent of the patient, and if it was not, the physician who failed in his legal duty is guilty of malpractice *no matter how skillfully the treatment may have been administered*

and the jury should determine the damages arising for the cobalt irradiation treatment. If the jury should find an informed consent was given by the patient for such treatment, the jury should next determine whether proper skill was used in administering the treatment.

Similar cases concerning the doctrine of "informed consent" include a recent New York case in which the plaintiff was being treated for rheumatoid arthritis by a series of gold injections and as a result developed a condition known as "exfoliate dermatitis." The court, in affirming a judgment for the plaintiff, stated:

> It also appeared that the medical profession recognized the possibility of undesirable reactions in the use of gold therapy. We are of the opinion that, under the facts and circumstances disclosed by this record, including the fact that no immediate emergency existed, defendant was obligated to make a reasonable disclosure to his patient of the known dangers which were incident to or possible in the proposed use of gold; and that the trial court, therefore, did not err in charging, in substance, that defendant could be found guilty of malpractice if he failed in that duty.

In another such case, it was held that the defendant was under a duty to disclose to the plaintiff the hazards of insulin shock therapy. The fact that the plaintiff's wife signed the written consent is not binding on the plaintiff where he claims he had no knowledge and did not authorize such signing.

The following are other illustrations of the same principle:

Where *aortography* (a diagnostic procedure performed by injection of contrast media so that the aorta can be X-rayed) resulted in paralysis of the lower extremities of plaintiff, a duty to inform plaintiff of the risks involved was recognized by the court.

In a case involving the removal of a small cyst on the neck, it was found during the operation (in which the patient was conscious) that the cyst was not small, but extended down to the facial nerve. The defendant injured this nerve, and it was held that he should have obtained plaintiff's consent before continuing further and should have informed her of the risk of nerve injury.

Where a prostate operation was performed and resulted in sterilization, the plaintiff was not told that the defendant would sever the spermatic cord. The court held that the defendant doctor was under a duty to inform—even though he claimed it was a necessary procedure to prevent infection—for the plaintiff had the right to decide whether to risk infection or be sterilized.

In a final and very interesting case, an arteriogram (a diagnostic procedure to X-ray cerebral arteries done by injection of contrast media) resulted in a child of nine becoming paralyzed. It was shown that complications arise in 3 percent of the cases involving this procedure, and since this was so, the appellate court held that it was an error to direct a verdict for the defendant doctor, as he was under a duty to obtain an informed consent from the parents.

8. It is improper for a doctor who is personally hired to perform an operation to delegate the operation to someone else or to stand by or merely guide the operation. This is what is known as "ghost" surgery.

PROXIMATE CAUSE

Proof that a doctor was guilty of a departure from proper medical practice is not enough. It must also be shown that the departure itself was the proximate cause of the injuries claimed. The patient may already have been treated for some ailment that causes him pain and disability; he must prove that the defendant's malpractice *caused, precipitated,* or *aggravated* his condition.

For example, let's assume that the plaintiff fractured his left leg in a fall. The defendant immobilized the fractures in a plaster-of-Paris cast, but, because the cast was applied too tightly, a disturbance in circulation occurred and the plaintiff developed a thrombophlebitis of the leg. For the plaintiff to win his case, he would not only have to prove that there had been a departure from accepted medical practice in the way that the cast was applied but also that it was the proximate cause of the complications that developed.

PARTNERS, ASSISTANTS, AND NURSES

It is important to note briefly that medical malpractice does not concern only the principal physician himself. Doctors may be liable not only for their own negligence but also for the negligent acts of their partners, assistants, agents, or even employees. Nurses can be held liable for their malpractice, and hospitals, of course, will be responsible for various negligent acts occurring within their jurisdiction.

Where doctors are partners in the practice of medicine, they "are all liable for an injury to a patient resulting from the lack of skill or the negligence . . . of any one of the partners within the scope of their partnership business." On the other hand, if a doctor merely recommends or sends another physician, he "is not liable for injuries resulting from the latter's want of skill or care."

Where there is more than one doctor on the case, the rule would appear to be:

1. ". . . a physician called *specially* and only for particular occasions is not liable for the negligent acts or omissions of another physician in his absence."

2. "A physician who merely arranges for an operation by

another . . . and lends casual assistance at the operation, is not jointly liable for the physician operating."

3. "A physician who merely administers an *anesthetic* to a patient operated on, is not liable for the negligence of the *operating* surgeon, and the operating surgeon is not liable for the negligence of the physician administering the anesthetic in his absence where each doctor has been employed to perform his separate work independently of the other."

An interesting exception here may be found in a New York case where the patient died following an operation because he had been given mismatched blood that was intended for another patient. In an action against the surgeon, anesthetist, and the hospital, the plaintiff obtained a verdict against *all three*. The appellate court affirmed the verdict even as against the surgeon, despite the fact that the *anesthetist* handled the details of the transfusion and admitted that it was his duty and not the surgeon's to check the blood. Though the surgeon had not ordered any blood, under the hospital rules *only he* was permitted to do so, so that when it arrived he should have suspected that something might have been wrong.

4. A physician is not liable for the negligence of hospital employees, such as interns, nurses, or orderlies, if he has no knowledge of their acts; an exception here would be a case where the negligent acts were performed under conditions where, in the exercise of ordinary care, he could have or should have been able to prevent their injurious effects and did not. "The mere fact that a physician or surgeon gives instructions to a hospital employee does not render the physician or surgeon liable for negligence of the hospital employee in carrying out the instruction."

A nurse is liable for her own acts of negligence in the same way as an intern or operating surgeon. Her employer, whether a doctor or a hospital, would be liable under the doctrine of *respondeat superior* for her negligence. At the operating table, for instance, the "scrub nurse" plays an important role, and usually has the responsibility of keeping the "sponge count." The operating surgeon might possibly escape liability, but, unquestionably, the hospital would be held liable for the negligence of its employee nurse.

This chapter has perforce been rather technical. But necessarily so. Medical malpractice deals with one of the most exacting of the professions; therefore, the nature of the liability must be carefully delineated, otherwise we shall be tilting at windmills.

There is much more that might have been said concerning the law of medical malpractice, but you now have the essentials. With them in mind, the cases that follow will be seen in better perspective. Because I am familiar with them— both how they were prepared and what happened at the trial —I have used cases drawn from my own experience.

III

HOSPITALS–WHEN ARE THEY LIABLE?

Two cases of malpractice by hospitals—and an examination of the law governing hospital liability

Shortly after the end of World War II, I was called in to try a most unusual case—one that strikingly revealed the inadequacies of the law governing hospital negligence at that time.

My client, John Harmon, had, as a youngster, been injured in a railroad accident and lost part of his right leg below the knee. He had been fitted with an artificial limb, and, as he said to me: "There was nothing I couldn't do. It was almost as good as my own."

Later, John Harmon had volunteered for the Merchant Marine and during the war attained the rank of lieutenant commander. In the invasion of France on D-Day, June 6, 1944, his ship had been one that was to form a beachhead of vessels; in the course of the landing he fell and painfully injured the stump of his amputated right leg. He described it at the trial as follows:

We pulled in, in the early hours of the morning along
with other ships that were to form a beachhead of ships
so that the landing of the troops would be easier, and
the ships were all loaded with dynamite ready to be
bombed, and the tugs came along and picked us up, and
while going overboard on the ladder one of the rungs
broke and I fell down fifteen feet to the deck of the
ship that came to take us off.

Two days later he was sent back to England, and then
he was returned to the United States, where, at the Maritime
Hospital, two reamputations of the same leg were done, this
time above the knee. To alleviate the intense pain involved
in the operative procedures and postoperative care, Commander Harmon had been given large doses of morphine.

This is how the difficulty began. Before very long, he became addicted to the drug.

On his return to New York, Commander Harmon heard
about the Mills Hospital, which specialized in the treatment
and cure of drug addicts. Anxious to cure himself of his
addiction, he voluntarily entered the hospital on May 1, 1945.
The treatment, which would cost $225, was to take two
weeks; it in part consisted of the daily injection of morphine
in reduced amounts until he would be weaned from the drug.

On about the twelfth day of his stay at the hospital, infection broke out at the site of the injections in both arms. Harmon become delirious at times, and was immediatley transferred to another hospital, where it was found that abscesses
had developed. He then had to undergo operations on both
of his arms, and was left with permanent scars.

An action was instituted against the Mills Hospital, charging them with negligence in the manner of giving the injections to the patient. Specifically, we claimed that there had
been a failure to use a sterilizing machine for the needles.

Our proof at the trial was that in the Utility Room there

was no sterilizing machine and that the nurse would sterilize the syringe and needles by placing them in a small pan of water, lighting the gas, and letting it come to a boil for a few minutes before turning the gas off. She would then give Commander Harmon an injection in either arm.

It was also shown that often the patient was the last on the floor to be treated and that the nurse would arrive with a tray of several syringes. Commander Harmon testified that "they just were rolling around on the tray instead of being on the cotton, the needle on the cotton to keep them clean." He further stated, concerning the needle itself: "Two or three times the needles doubled up, and I told her that the needles are a little dull and she says, 'Your skin is hard.' I said, 'No,' and she says, 'I will try to get some new needles.'"

We called as our expert Dr. Morris Steiner, who affirmed that in May, 1945, the accepted practice in hospitals in New York City was to sterilize hyperdermic needles by the use of a device called an autoclave, a self-closing appliance utilizing steam under pressure. (It is frequently seen today in a dentist's office.) Dr. Steiner further testified that sterilization by boiling medical instruments in water in open air was an *inadequate* and *improper* procedure because not all the germs and spores were killed by that method. He stated that even greater care in sterilizing was required when the needles were to be used in injecting drug addicts because their skin was devitalized and hence more subject to infection.

Finally, Dr. Steiner testified that the boiling method that was actually used was improper *even as a boiling method* because such a procedure required retention of the instruments in boiling water for at least twenty minutes.

At the completion of this testimony and a showing that there had been a departure from good hospital practice by the defendant, the plaintiff rested his case.

It is incumbent upon a plaintiff to make out a prima facie (on its face) case of liability against a defendant by the time he completes his proof. But once his attorney announces to the court, "Your Honor, the plaintiff rests," he must then stand or fall on whether he has established the defendant's negligence and his own freedom from contributory negligence (if that be an issue). At this juncture, the trial judge must view the plaintiff's proof in its most favorable light; he is even obliged to assume that it is true.

Then the defendant's attorney will come forward with a motion to dismiss the complaint, usually on the ground that there has been a failure of proof—that is, that the plaintiff has not shown one or more of the essential elements to establish the defendant's liability.

The defense attorney did just this in the case of Commander Harmon, arguing, in effect, that a hospital is not liable for the "medical" acts of its employees, but only their "administrative" acts—that is, if *treatment* was involved there could be no responsibility on the part of the hospital, even though negligently performed.

My opponent's motion was as follows:

> I move to dismiss the complaint on the ground that the plaintiff has failed to establish facts sufficient to constitute a cause of action, and on the further ground that the plaintiff has failed to show any negligence or malpractice on the part of the hospital, and that if there was any negligence it was on the part of the *nurse*, and under the cases, in the performance of her *professional duties*, the hospital would not be liable.

The defense attorney also called the court's attention to a case that held, in substance, that "where a nurse, acting in her *professional* capacity, fails to do something that should be done or does something in an improper manner, the hospital is not liable."

When he finished, the following exchange transpired:

THE COURT. Have you anything to say, Mr. Kramer?

MR. KRAMER. Does Your Honor wish to hear me?

THE COURT. Yes, just briefly.

The court's remark that he wanted to hear from me "just briefly" was an ominous sign. But I said:

> Insofar as the objection that they are not responsible for the acts of a nurse in that a nurse is a nonadministrative employee is concerned, I wish to point out that in that regard the plaintiff has proved an *administrative* act of negligence in that the hospital failed to furnish the nurse sterilizing equipment which, under our proof, is the standard method of sterilization.

Though I felt that, in accordance with the law in New York as it then existed, we had shown an "administrative" rather than a "medical" act of negligence, the court thought otherwise.

The judge granted my opponent's motion to dismiss the plaintiff's case with these words:

> Even assuming that the failure or the omission on the part of the nurse was the proximate cause of the plaintiff's injuries, it is not sufficient to hold the hospital. The acts of the nurse were performed in the course of *medical treatment* and not in the capacity of a servant doing administrative work.

We were shocked. So, probably, are you. There seemed an apparent injustice in the summary dismissal of Commander Harmon's case.

Later, an appeal was taken to a higher court, which reversed the dismissal on the grounds urged by the plaintiff, namely, that the hospital's negligence was "administrative" rather than "medical." Though the case was thereafter settled, it pointed up an existing confusion.

It might be interesting at this point to trace the law concerning the liability of hospital to patient, for even in an enlightened state such as New York, it has been markedly slow in its development.

Up until about sixty years ago (1910 to be exact), if the defendant hospital was a "charitable" hospital (nonprofit), even though "administrative" negligence could be shown, no recovery could be had against it: not by a patient who was a recipient of charity, *nor even by a stranger*. The reason advanced for this policy was stated by one court as follows:

> The public policy which forms the basis of the rule should be as broad as the situations it is intended to cover. It is designed to protect charity from claims of litigation. As between the dispenser of public benevolence and the unfortunate victim of negligence, the law has determined to protect the former at the expense of the latter. As a matter of public policy, no distinctions based upon logic or expediency can be made between administrative acts and non-administrative acts. A public policy, so explicitly enunciated, must be permitted to function in a vital manner to carry out the ends for which it was designed.

However, back in 1910, a mechanic by the name of Hordern was hired to make repairs on a boiler on the premises of the Salvation Army and because of a defect in it he was injured. One of the main defenses to the action was that the Salvation Army is a charitable corporation and therefore immune from liability. The lower courts dismissed the plaintiff's case on that ground. But the Court of Appeals reversed the dismissal and ordered a new trial, saying that while "it is recognized that the *beneficiary* of a charitable trust may not hold the corporation liable for the neglect of its servants," the court was of the opinion that this exemption of liability should not extend to the plaintiff since *he was not a recipient of the charity*.

But there was still no remedy for a *patient*, no matter what the negligence of a nonprofit hospital—at least not until 1937. (It is hard to realize that this was so a scant thirty years ago!) At this time, a patient named Catherine Sheehan was being taken home from the North County Community Hospital by ambulance when the vehicle collided with another car, injuring the patient.

The Court of Appeals—which is the highest appellate court in New York—then decided to change the policy that had for so long been in effect. In a leading decision, the court, per Mr. Justice Loughran, wrote:

> On the other side it is answered that the "waiver" doctrine is pretty much a fiction; that to impose liability is to beget careful management; and that no conception of justice demands that an exception to the rule of *respondeat superior* be made in favor of the resources of a charity and against the person of a beneficiary injured by the tort of a mere servant or employee functioning in that character. It is our judgment that the great weights are in this scale.

The court then went on to say that it would not be a "harmonious policy" if the plaintiff had to "put up with her injuries on the score that the appellant is a charitable corporation."

Now the door was finally open for patients to sue a hospital. But a new roadblock was soon created: It was determined that the hospital could be held liable only for "administrative" acts of negligence and not for "medical" acts. The rationale for this rule was succinctly stated by one court when it decided: "Such a hospital undertakes, not to heal or attempt to heal through the agency of others, but merely to *supply* others who will heal or attempt to heal on their *own* responsibility."

The effect of this rule was to cause all kinds of legal gymnastics and confusion in the courts. Some judges held a particular act as "medical" with no liability, while another held the same act as "administrative" with the hospital liable. For example, if a patient had been given the wrong type of blood transfusion and died as a result of the mismatched blood, was it medical or administrative? It was anybody's guess. In one case it was held that where an *orderly* placed a hot-water bottle against a patient's body and she was burned, that was an "administrative" act; yet the same thing done by a *nurse* was held to be a "medical" act.

It was during this chaotic state of the law that, as recently as 1957, the highest court of New York State rendered the landmark decision of *Bing v. Thunig*.

In one fell swoop this decision abolished the artificial distinction between "medical" and "administrative" acts and held that it does not make any difference what the act is if it was performed by any employee of the hospital—be he a doctor, a nurse, an orderly, or a porter. "Hospitals should, in short, shoulder the responsibilities borne by everyone else," the court said. "There is no reason to continue their exemption from the universal law of *respondeat superior*."

Thus, today in New York State and in most other states, a hospital *is* liable to a patient for the negligent acts of its employees and it matters not that they are a nonprofit, private, or municipal corporation. However, there still are about twenty states in which the patient has no remedy against a charitable hospital.

As for the liability of governmental agencies, since 1946, by enactment of the Federal Tort Claims Act, the United States Government has been liable for the negligent acts of its employees in government hospitals. Prior to that date, a patient had no remedy at law, and was relegated to trying to get a special Act passed by Congress.

Long before the Federal Government waived its immunity from liability, the State of New York did so in 1928; this waiver has since been held to apply to all cities, counties, villages, and townships that operate hospitals in the state.

Since the turn of the century, when practically no liability existed in favor of a patient against a hospital, we have come almost full circle. No longer is the issue "Do you have a *right* to sue?"—but rather, the more sensible question "Is there *merit* to the claim?"

A hospital will also be liable for the acts of its "specialists," such as its anesthesiologists, radiologists, and pathologists, if they are employees of the hospital. If they are not employees, but operate under some concession arrangements or enjoy a monopoly of a particular department of the hospital, the hospital may still be liable for the negligence of such specialists.

A hospital is not liable for injury to patients by reason of carrying out orders of *attending* physicians as long as reasonable care is used by the employees.

In brief, the duty of a hospital to its patients is to furnish the patient with diligent and skillful care, competent attendants, and safe equipment. Accordingly, hospitals have been held liable for the following:

1. failure to admit a patient when they should have;
2. prematurely discharging a patient or improperly moving the patient from one hospital to another when this resulted in her death;
3. leaving a patient unattended in a delivery room so that she fell off a bed which had no sideboards;
4. failure to exercise "reasonable care in the selection and maintenance of equipment and facilities furnished" to the patient.
5. failure to supervise properly a patient who is in the de-

livery room and becomes mentally deranged, or has shown evidence of mental instability;

6. giving the patient mismatched blood or other improper medication;

7. permitting a patient to be burned with a hot-water bottle, heat lamp, or similar device;

8. failure of a resident at a hospital to notify the treating doctor *promptly* of "significant adverse change" in the patient's condition.

Let us now consider another case of hospital negligence, one that resulted in a tragedy of the highest order.

Mrs. Phyllis Macon, a young woman of twenty, had been married a little over a year, and was pregnant. She had always been in good health, and her prenatal period went so smoothly that all her friends remarked on how beautifully she was carrying her first child.

Just before Christmas of 1958, in her ninth month, Mrs. Macon's water broke and she was taken to the Burnside Memorial Hospital. Later that same day she was delivered of a child—but within a few minutes she started to bleed profusely. Her blood type was O-RH Negative; it is a universal type of blood, not rare, and about 15 percent of all people have it.

The next day, because the hospital did not have this blood type available in time, Mrs. Phyllis Macon was dead.

The case came on for trial before the Honorable Samuel S. Leibowitz and a jury in 1965.

In my opening statement to the jury, I said that we would show that the doctor was calling for blood but that all the hospital had was *one pint*—and that was not even on the maternity floor but in the blood bank in the hospital laboratory. We would further show that it took a full forty-five minutes from the time Mrs. Macon went into shock until the time the first pint of blood came up from the laboratory and that even then the doctor called for more. It just wasn't there.

Then I began to describe to the jury the tragic and chaotic events that took place when the seriousness of Mrs. Macon's condition was recognized. The picture was no less than a nightmare:

> Now everyone started to run around. The family, the father of the girl, the husband, the relatives now started to panic, running around to hospitals in the city to find blood. The second pint arrived and was given *three-quarters* of an hour after the first, so that she did not get the second pint of blood until an *hour and a half* after she went into shock.
>
> We are going to prove to you that she needed those two pints of blood *immediately*, within a matter of minutes after she had gone into shock. . . . We will show you that what happened to this girl occurred because if you don't get that blood in time, you then go into *irreversible* shock. In other words, the brain and the kidney and the other vital organs of the body now are so lost and not getting oxygen that they just start dying. Although, eventually they finally got more blood and more blood pumped into her—in fact, eventually they pumped ten pints of blood into her—it was of no value any more. What happened here was that there was too little blood given and what was given was given too late. Mrs. Macon hung on as long as she could. . . .

In his opening, the hospital's attorney took the position that the hospital had in fact not done anything wrong. He claimed that they were merely carrying out the orders of the patient's own doctor and that it was not their responsibility to have the blood available.

As my first witness I called Dr. Paul Longrin, who had delivered the patient. Dr. Longrin was the Director of Obstetrics at the hospital and had been named as a codefendant.

I asked the doctor whether it was a fact that within a few minutes after delivery the patient hemorrhaged and then, a few minutes later, went into shock. He testified that this was correct. My questioning proceded as follows:

> Q. Doctor, when a person is in shock, as Mrs. Macon was, because of loss of blood, is it vital that the blood be replaced and pumped into her immediately?
> A. As fast as we could get it.
> Q. I am not asking you about how fast you can get it; but if you have it available, you would insert that blood immediately, would you not, Doctor?
> A. I would.
> THE COURT. You mean the faster, the better?
> THE WITNESS. The faster, the better.
> Q. When you saw that she was in shock, what did you do about blood?
> A. I didn't wait to see whether she was in shock. As soon as I saw the blood pouring out I called for blood.

The doctor then told of how he asked the intern and nurse to get the blood, which was kept in the laboratory two floors below.

> Q. Doctor, was it then within a matter of a few minutes after the afterbirth came out that you requested blood from either the intern or the nurse; is that what you are saying?
> A. That is correct.
> Q. How long was it, or what time was it that the first pint of blood arrived for Mrs. Macon?
> A. I think the record shows it was either 8:30 or 8:45.
> Q. Was it a matter then of about 45 minutes before the first pint of blood arrived for Mrs. Macon?

A. The record will show that.

Dr. Longrin went on to testify how only the one pint of blood arrived after an initial delay of forty-five minutes and how the second pint did not arrive until forty-five minutes later. Mrs. Macon, he testified, continued to receive blood throughout the night, at different hours, and eventually received about ten pints of blood.

He admitted that he had written into the hospital record: "Unfortunately, the bulk of this blood arrived when the patient was in *irreversible shock*."

He also admitted that unfortunately they only *"had one pint"* of blood.

The questioning of Dr. Longrin ended as follows:

Q. What was the cause of her death, Doctor?
A. The primary fact was the massive loss of blood.
Q. In other words, then, what you call postpartum hemorrhage?
A. That is correct.
Q. She bled to death; is that what happened to her?
A. As it turned out, you probably would say that.
Q. Were there any other contributing causes?
A. Then you will add to that as a foundation or a basis the fact that the blood did not clot.
Q. That is a condition of afibrinogenemia, and that was a complication that came about because of the fact that she had bled so extensively and there had been inadequate blood replacement?
A. The condition resulted from a massive loss of blood.
THE COURT. You haven't answered the question, Doctor. You spoke of a primary cause?
THE WITNESS. That is correct, sir.
THE COURT. Was there a secondary cause or a contributing cause?

THE WITNESS. The contributing cause, of course, is this lack of clotting power.

THE COURT. Can you state with reasonable medical certainty what that was due to?

THE WITNESS. I would say it was due to the massive loss of blood.

THE COURT. Was it due to the failure to *replace* this blood?

THE WITNESS. I would say—I would answer it this way, sir: that the fact that they could not replace sufficient blood would aggravate or perpetuate or continue that condition.

THE COURT. Was that a contributing cause to this woman's death?

THE WITNESS. I would think yes.

At this point it was patently clear that the defendant had, in fact, no legitimate defense. As a result, the case went no further, for a settlement satisfactory to all parties was agreed upon.

Actually, had the case not been settled at this juncture, and had I been put to my proof, I was prepared to show that the delay in the arrival of *even the first pint of blood* was inexcusable, for the accepted and proper practice is that the blood be kept on the *maternity* floor and not elsewhere.

Dr. J. Robert Willson, a Professor of Obstetrics and Gynecology at Temple University School of Medicine, states this principle emphatically in his book *Management of Obstetric Difficulties*. It is essential, he writes, that "at least *two* units of RH Negative type O blood should be stored in a refrigerator *near delivery room* for administration to patients in whom bleeding is so profuse that it is impractical to delay transfusion until the usual crossmatch can be set up."

But the hospital had not complied with this principle— and a woman was dead—an unnecessary sacrifice at the altar of carelessness.

IV

"FOR WANT OF A NAIL . . ."

*A look at some malpractice cases involving
anesthesia, orthopedics, and diagnostic
procedures*

        Since the malpractice case does
not readily lend itself to settlement, a lawyer in this type of
litigation must be prepared to see the case through to its bitter
end. He can expect an exhausting, expensive process, and
therefore, unless there is genuine merit to the claim, it will be
unrewarding and should not be undertaken. In subsequent
chapters, various kinds of medical malpractice cases—particularly those involving complications of surgery—will be presented in great detail, from beginning to end. However, some
important cases are settled before they go to jury verdict. A
number of these are presented here in brief form; each concerns one of the three main categories into which most malpractice cases fall: *Anesthesia, Orthopedics,* and *Diagnostic
procedures.*

ANESTHESIA

A person about to undergo an operation is invariably careful in the selection of a surgeon. He will make inquiry about

him from doctor friends and may even ask someone to check the surgeon's qualifications. In many states, including New York, the Medical Society publishes a medical directory that lists every doctor by name and presents such pertinent information as his medical training, his specialty (if any), and his current hospital affiliations. Though such a directory cannot tell you how *competent* a doctor is, it does serve to assure you that he is generally *qualified* to perform the required surgery.

But few people check on their anesthesiologist, though from the point of view of hazards involved, he is as important as, if not more important than, the surgeon. Unquestionably, more complications occur during the course of anesthesia than from the surgery itself. A patient who submits to general anesthesia literally places his life in the hands of the anesthetist, and unless the doctor is competent to handle the many complications that might develop, the results could be catastrophic. Regional anesthesia (such as spinal) or even local (such as an injection of novocaine to deaden pain) can also be highly dangerous.

Dr. Joseph Artusio, Jr., and Dr. Valentine Mazzia, two outstanding authorities in this field, say in their book *Practical Anesthesiology:* "Anesthesia is always a serious business. There is no minor anesthesia. Each time an individual is rendered unconscious by an anesthetic, there is a danger that he may not awaken. One can never afford to be casual in the administration of an anesthetic. It requires, at all times, an active alert mind." They also make this significant observation, which bears directly on our concern with medical negligence: "Most complications occurring during general anesthesia are *preventable.* They usually arise because the individual administering the anesthesia is unaware of the possibility of a complication or, if he is aware of a possible complication, has paid insufficient attention to the details of administering the general anesthetic."

The ideal, of course, would be to have the anesthetic given by a *physician* anesthesiologist. Unfortunately, there are too few of them, so that in some hospitals, especially in smaller communities, the anesthesia is administered by a *nurse* anesthetist. Many of these nurses are competent, though obviously lacking the breadth of knowledge that a physician anesthesiologist has; few are as qualified to treat any serious complication that might develop.

Most of the difficulties that do develop are the result of sheer neglect. For example, one of the *mandatory* requirements is that the patient be visited by the anesthesiologist *at least* one day before the operation so that he may, first, determine the physical condition of the patient; second, make an estimate of the operative risk; third, decide which anesthetic and technique should be used. Too often, however, the first time the anesthetist sees his patient is in the operating room. This is much too late. Innumerable problems can arise by this time. Strangely, the worst offender is sometimes the experienced anesthetist, because he is too busy and feels he needs but little time to evaluate a patient's condition. In addition, the patient must be watched carefully in the Recovery Room until he has reacted from the anesthesia; if there are any complications at this time, extreme caution must be exercised.

In each of the following cases, various types of complications arising from negligent anesthetic procedures may be observed. The severity of the first, which occurred after a hysterectomy, will alert you dramatically to the dangers involved.

Alice Dunne, age forty-one, mother of three children and in general good health, had noticed excessive bleeding at her last menstrual period. Her gynecologist had her admitted to the hospital for a simple procedure known as a "scraping" of the womb. But while performing the "D and C," as the treatment is called, the doctor found that the uterus was enlarged and that fibroids, or growths, were present; he then *elected* to remove the womb by performing a hysterectomy. This was done under a general anesthetic, and at the completion of the operation, at 1:00 P.M., the patient was transferred to the Recovery Room.

The surgeon's notes show that "Patient left the O.R. in good condition"; but the notes of the nurse in the Recovery Room show that about the same time, 1:00 P.M., the patient was having difficulty in breathing—reported as "Respiration, labored and moist."

Mrs. Dunne's condition began to deteriorate. She started to run a temperature; her breathing became more labored, and despite various types of medication she died two days later. The cause of death was given as "bilateral bronchopneumonia," and because the husband refused to give his consent for an autopsy to be performed, a more definitive diagnosis could not be made.

An action in behalf of the husband and children was brought against the gynecologist, Dr. Harrison, and the two anesthetists, Dr. Arntz and Dr. Ball, who were partners. In an examination before trial of Dr. Arntz, it was learned that

1. the first time he saw the patient was in the operating room, about fifteen minutes before the operation began;

2. he looked at the chart, spoke to the patient, but did not examine her;

3. about fifteen minutes after surgery had begun, the patient developed "a little difficulty in ventilating," which he reported to the surgeon—and it then cleared up;

4. during the operation he was relieved by his partner, Dr. Ball, who took over the role of anesthesiologist because, as Dr. Arntz said, "I had a very severe case previously and I was exhausted, tired."

A definite picture was emerging. It became even clearer through the examination before trial of Dr. Ball, which showed that

1. the first time he ever saw the patient was about one hour *after* the operation had started, at which time he relieved Dr. Arntz (the operation continued for another hour);

2. he saw the patient for a minute or two in the Recovery Room; she seemed satisfactory, and he left her;

3. about three hours later he was called back to the Recovery Room by the nurse—the patient was "mildly cyanotic," and he suctioned her throat;

4. he spoke to the gynecologist on the phone and then agreed to watch the patient, which he did (on and off) for about two more hours, from 4: P.M. until 6:00 P.M.—at which time he went *home;*

5. when he left the patient—never to see her again, dead or alive—her condition was about the same as when he saw her at 4:00 P.M.: "mildly cyanotic."

The whole sad story was now virtually complete: It required only the examination before trial of the gynecologist, Dr. Harrison. The information that came forth at this meeting was most significant. It showed that

1. in the course of the operation, Dr. Harrison did *not* know and was not told of any "difficulty in ventilating" (contrary to what the anesthetist had said;

2. a few minutes after the patient was brought to the Recovery Room, her respiration was moist and labored (which is abnormal), and he used the suction apparatus on her;

3. he left the patient and the hospital shortly past 1:00 P.M., after the anesthesiologist told him she would be better "in a moment or two";

4. about three or four hours later he was notified by phone that her condition had worsened, and he had a discussion *on the phone* with the anesthesiologist;

5. he came back to the hospital at 9:00 P.M., after Mrs. Dunne had been in the Recovery Room some eight hours, and noted that her condition was worse.

It is important to note that when Dr. Harrison left her at 1:00 P.M. she was in some difficulty; that three hours later she was in more trouble; and that from 6:00 P.M. (when the anesthesiologist left) until 9:00 P.M., neither the surgeon nor the anesthesiologist was in attendance of the patient—*who was in grave danger.*

This case is almost classical in its facts, for here we see: the failure of the anesthesiologist to see the patient at least one day before the operation; the failure of the surgeon and anesthesiologist to work as a team; the dangerous substitution of anesthesiologists *in the middle* of the operation—with the first one starting out exhausted rather than alert—and finally, the failure to supervise the patient properly while she remained in the Recovery Room. And the result? A mother of three children dead because of medical negligence.

For various reasons, anesthesia problems, which are not seen in elective surgery, often occur in *obstetrics.* Normally, a patient will enter a hospital the day before the planned surgery. This gives the staff time not only to perform all the necessary laboratory work but also to control the food intake so that if general anesthesia is to be given the stomach will be empty. Food in the stomach during general anesthesia may cause the patient to vomit and even choke to death. Such happened in the case of Mrs. Mary Reiner.

Mrs. Reiner was thirty-seven years old and had one two-year-old child. Again pregnant, she had come to full term without difficulty. One evening about 8:00 P.M. she began to feel steady labor pains, and went to the hospital about an hour later. At 11 P.M. she was taken to the delivery room where a nurse-anesthetist, under the doctor's supervision, gave her a general anesthetic of nitrous oxide and ether. Fifteen minutes later she delivered a normal boy weighing eight pounds and two ounces, but at the moment of delivery she coughed, brought up vomit, became cyanotic, and choked to death a few minutes later.

An autopsy was performed by the Medical Examiner of the City of New York, and the cause of death was officially given as "asphyxiation from aspiration of gastric content;

death during nitrous oxide and ether anesthesia for delivery purposes." About four hours before she had been admitted to the hospital, Mrs. Reiner had had a meal of steak, asparagus, and potatoes.

Vomiting is a major factor in maternal deaths occurring during general anesthesia (about 40 percent of all maternal deaths), and may also be an important complication in general surgery. The sad fact, though, is that in almost every instance it is a complication that *can be prevented*. The stomach can be emptied by mechanical means; vomiting can be induced prior to the giving of general anesthesia; or, especially in maternity cases, a "regional" or "conduction" anesthesia, such as a spinal block, can be used instead of general anesthesia. Literally hundreds of women *who are in the best of health* die unnecessarily each year because some doctors or nurses do not use the anesthesia properly.

But general anesthesia is not the only kind that can be dangerous. Anesthetic complications involving regional or spinal anesthesia, as in this unfortunate story of Marvin Sutpen, can be equally fatal.

Sutpen, a married man fifty-two years old, with one child, had been in excellent health all his life; he could not recall ever having been seriously ill. However, in recent months he noticed some blood in his stool. A rectal examination revealed a small external hemorrhoid; surgery was advised, and he was soon admitted to the hospital. The following day he was taken to the operating room.

The anesthesiologist attempted to give the usual spinal anesthesia, but it did not take. Then the surgeon and anesthesiologist tried caudal anesthesia with Xylocaine, which was only partially successful. And finally Sutpen was given a second injection of Xylocaine, but this time a massive dose that sent him into convulsions and coma. He died a few days later. An autopsy later revealed that death was caused by "convulsions and coma following caudal and subcutaneous injection of Xylocaine for hemorrhoidectomy."

The medical chart showed that the patient had been given various amounts of Xylocaine, but it was hard to determine exactly what the dosage had been. However, the anesthesiologist had made this revealing entry: "Heretofore the dosage Dr. Arvin used was always within the recommended maximum dose. Based upon past experience and his usage of the drug Xylocaine, *my questioning him on the amount he used seemed to be superfluous at the time.*"

Any comment on the underlined portion of the entry would seem to be "superfluous."

A healthy man had entered the hospital for a minor operation; because an anesthesiologist had thought it unnecessary to question the dosage of a drug, Marvin Sutpen's wife was now a widow and his child fatherless.

ORTHOPEDICS

The care and treatment of injuries and diseases involving bones and joints is known as orthopedics. The treatment of broken bones and spinal surgery, as well as other orthopedic surgery, is an everyday affair, but care and caution must *always* be.exercised by the "orthopedic surgeon." Dr. Edward L. Compere, a leading authority in this field, has succinctly noted: "Any error [by the doctor] may result in deformity or a crippling defect. He must take every safeguard which will protect his patients against any injury that can be attributed to the *treatment* itself."

Every now and then, however, the unusual will take place in orthopedic work. Such was the case with little Angela Gaines, who had been born with a congenital dislocation of the *left* hip.

Quite a few children are born with this condition, in which

the hip bone is out of the pelvic socket, and it is treated either by casting or surgery, or both. The results are usually excellent, and most children are restored to normal.

When Angela was one year old, she was under the care of an orthopedic surgeon who placed her in a body cast. The casts were changed several times during the following year, but at the end of that time the doctor was not satisfied with the result. He advised the parents that surgery was necessary, and soon afterward the child was admitted to a hospital. There an operation known as a "subtrochanteric osteotomy" was performed by the orthopedic surgeon on her hip, and another cast was applied.

When Mrs. Gaines came in to see her child shortly after the operation, and saw that the cast was on the *right* leg she fainted. The operation had been performed on the wrong hip. As it developed, not only had a normal hip been opened up, but a plate with four screws had been inserted in that hip joint.

The unnecessary suffering this child and her parents had to endure is difficult to put in words. And why? Yes, why?

The second orthopedic case I want to describe may also seem to be in the realm of fiction: Unfortunately for the patient, it was all too true.

Mrs. Arlene Windsor, who was fifty years old and in good health, had, while attending a function at a catering hall, slipped and fallen on the dance floor. She was taken at once to a nearby hospital where it was found that she had broken her hip. An orthopedic surgeon was called in, and about one week later a major operative procedure was performed whereby the upper end of the thigh bone was removed and an artificial head (called an Austin-Moore prosthesis) inserted. This is a metallic rounded head that has a stem attached to it, which is driven into the shaft of the bone. In order to make sure that the stem has been properly inserted into the bone, the whole procedure is done under X-*ray control*. This enables the doctor to know whether the stem is correctly inserted.

The hospital record showed that "lateral [side] films were *requested* but were not secured due to *technical* difficulties." Just what this meant was not clear until we got a chance to question the doctor at an examination-before-trial.

It turned out that *"technical* difficulties" meant that the X-ray technician *did not know how to take the lateral film.* He tried several shots, but they were all unsatisfactory. The surgeon then called the X-ray department. He told them to send someone up to the operating room quickly, someone who would know how to take a proper lateral X ray, since the patient was lying on the table with her hip already opened and the prosthesis partially inserted into the bone.

Here are the actual questions that were posed, and the surgeon's answers:

Q. What was there about the X rays that was unsatisfactory?

A. As I said, the X ray did not show the stem and did not show the head.

Q. Doctor, does that mean that the film was not taken of the stem and head, or does that mean that the film was so unclear that one could not see the stem and head?

A. The area involved was taken, but I must try to explain that a lateral view is much more difficult technically to take in the operating room. One has to be careful of asepsis, of sterility of the field and this is much more difficult than the AP view or the lateral taken in the X-Ray Department itself, and this technician was *unable* to give me a satisfactory view.

Q. Did you request further views before proceeding with the operation?

A. I requested further views, but I reached the point where I also requested help from the Department of

X Rays itself. The man who was in the operating room was not a—I don't know what his qualifications were, but he just couldn't get the X Ray and that's all I was interested in. I knew there was another man who had more experience in this particular technique and I asked for him and couldn't get him. He wasn't available.

Q. Of whom did you ask?

A. I was operating. I asked the nurse to call the X-Ray Department to get the director of the hospital—of the X-ray Department, and the only one that she could get was one of the other technicians and nobody came up. I just couldn't get anybody up to the operating room; impossible.

Q. How long a period did this take?

A. I think it was at least an hour.

Q. During that time had you stopped operating?

A. Of course.

Q. Were you just waiting there?

A. I waited until I could possibly see that someone would come up, but I could not get any response.

Q. No message?

A. The message was they were too busy at one time; that they didn't have any technician at another time, nobody else was available at the third time, and *I simply was frustrated.* I couldn't take the X ray myself. I couldn't get proper help to show me what the film looked like and finally I had to proceed.

The doctor testified there was a delay of over one hour; since he could not wait any longer, he continued the operation without the benefit of the essential X rays. "I proceeded with the surgery," he said, "and I was able to finish the operation *without knowing* where the stem of the prosthesis was."

Unfortunately for the patient, the stem was not in its

proper place; it was sticking out into the sciatic nerve. This was learned a few days later when, after the patient kept complaining about severe pain, a proper lateral film was finally taken.

The patient continued to complain of severe pain in the hip and leg, and about two months later she was taken back into the operating room for the purpose of having the protruding stem removed. This was to be done with an electric saw, but something unexpected happened. A resident doctor was holding back the muscles and nerves of the thigh with a *retractor* when, just as the saw reached the stem, the retractor *slipped* from his hands. As a result, the surgeon severed the sciatic nerve.

And was this second error, a severe one, clearly set forth in the hospital record? Scarcely. In fact, it was reported in this innocent way: "Using an electric saw with a diamond saw-blade, the prosthetic stem was cut as it emerged from the shaft of the femur. . . . The laceration of the sciatic nerve was found to be *further extended* during the process of removing the stem."

Not a word was said about the *slipping* of a retractor; but when the sworn testimony of the surgeon was obtained, he admitted: "There was a retractor involved, and the retractor *slipped* during the course of the procedure and the nerve was further damaged."

As a result of this second operative complication, with further injury to the sciatic nerve, the patient developed a dropped foot that was frightfully painful. Because of it, she had to wear a special brace and shoe. Thereafter, Mrs. Windsor was in and out of other hospitals for treatment of the severe complications that had occurred. She began to take narcotics, and then continued to do so—to kill the pain caused by the injury to the nerve. After a year she still could not bear weight on the leg. She became discouraged and despondent. And then one morning Mrs. Windsor could stand it no longer: she took a plastic bag, placed it over her head, and snuffed out her life.

The final orthopedic case involves the failure to reduce a broken bone properly, and then to apply a cast correctly. The fracture of a bone is a common injury arising from many kinds of accidents. How well that broken bone is reduced—that is, put back in its normal position as closely as possible, and then properly immobilized—will determine whether or not recovery will be satisfactory.

Here is what happened to Alan Besant.

While at work he fell and broke his ankle. He was taken to the emergency room of a leading hospital at eight-thirty of that Saturday evening. There he was seen by a resident doctor, who ordered X rays. These were taken, and showed that the patient had sustained severe fractures of the bones of the ankle, with displacement of the fragments. The medical description of his injury was: "trimalleolar fracture of the left tibia and fibula, with *broadening* of the ankle mortise, posterior *displacement* of the distal fibular fragment, and downward and anterior *displacement* of the medial malleolar fragment."

Simply stated, the bones of the ankle were broken in three places and also displaced or pushed out of their normal position.

Mr. Besant was admitted to the hospital, and the resident tried to reach the attending physician in charge of the service. He tried both the physician's home and office but, as he testified, "I couldn't get in touch with him at this time; he was out. I don't know where he was." It is a well-recognized rule of orthopedics that the first eight to ten hours after a fracture (especially when serious, like this one was) are the most important because the muscles, ligaments, and other soft tissue around the fracture site have not yet begun to set and are thus more amenable to the satisfactory reduction of the fracture. Unable after two or three hours to reach the attending surgeon, the resident applied a plaster cast, *without first reducing*—that is, attempting to get the broken bones back into normal position.

The next day, Sunday, when the attending surgeon in charge of the Fracture Service claims to have arrived at the hospital, he noted: "Position in cast not satisfactory. Will reduce under anesthesia." Oddly, although the operation chart was dated as of Sunday, the anesthesia chart and nurse's notes both showed that it wasn't until *Monday* that Mr. Besant was operated on.

In any event, the first cast had to be removed, and some forty-eight hours after the original injury the surgeon undertook to reduce the fractures. After the operation on the ankle was complete, a second cast was applied. But now a new complication developed. The patient, as soon as the new cast was applied, kept complaining that he had pain on the plantar surface—the sole of his foot.

Two days later the hospital recorded this entry concerning Mr. Besant: "Cast tight. Cut at foot and loosened and then replastered." But the patient continued to complain about the cast; and about three weeks later, when the cast was cut open, it was found that there was an area of ulceration; this area later became necrotic and gangrenous.

What finally happened?

Alan Besant had to be transferred to another hospital where one toe was completely amputated and part of another removed. He was confined to this second hospital for almost three months and was out of work for about one year.

It is interesting to speculate that Alan Besant might have been better off if he had gotten his original injury on some far-off island, where he could not have gotten this kind of medical treatment. It has been estimated that nature or time itself will heal or at least improve 75 percent of our ailments.

Those aren't bad odds.

DIAGNOSTIC PROCEDURES

All of us have, at one time or another, undergone a diagnostic test, a test performed to aid the doctor in his diagnosis. A large number of these involve X rays of such organs as the brain (angiogram), urinary system (intravenous pyelogram), or digestive system (gastrointestinal series). Since these areas do not show up on the X ray, it is necessary that some contrast medium be used. Here is where the trouble lies, since some people are allergic or sensitive to this material. A tragic example of how dangerous this can be is to be found in the chapter "Doomed to Die?"; in that case, a patient undergoing an intravenous pyelogram developed convulsions—and died.

Another category of diagnostic tests includes the use of instruments that are inserted through the mouth to check on some condition of the lungs or of the passageway to the stomach—the bronchoscopy or esophagoscopy. At the other end we have the proctoscope or sigmoidoscope. Sometimes these instruments are used to snip off a piece of tissue, a biopsy, so that it can be studied for possible malignancy.

Unfortunately, complications can and do occur in the course of these procedures, which are not treatment but merely tests to aid the doctor in his diagnosis. My experience has been that most diagnostic procedures that result in severe injury or death are due to *carelessness*. The standard medical defense to this type of case is that it was "unavoidable," that in the "best" hands you can get this kind of "unusual" or "untoward" reaction. Maybe so. But overlooking for the moment the fact that even the "best" doctor can be careless in a given case, the law in its wisdom has in recent years been invoking the doctrine of "informed consent."

I have referred to "informed consent" in an earlier chapter, but a description of the doctrine is worth repeating. In effect, it provides that any doctor who undertakes to perform a procedure, whether it be for treatment or for disgnostic purposes only, but especially as to the latter, should tell the patient if there are *any possible risks* to his life or health involved. It is a rule of common sense, for the patient can thus make up his mind—with knowledge of the risks involved—whether or not he wants to submit to a particular procedure. The rationale, a wise one, is that "each man is considered to be master of his own body and he may, if he is of sound mind, expressly prohibit the performance of life-saving surgery, or other medical treatment. . . ."

"Informed consent" does not mean that every time a surgeon is about to perform an operation he must tell the patient that even though he does nothing wrong the patient may develop an "infection" or "hemorrhage." Of course not. But, following a *routine* prostatectomy patients have been known to develop severe urinary leakage or sexual impotence. And following a *routine* hysterectomy there have been injuries to the bladder—with development of a fistula and urinary leakage. There can be no greater suffering—or shame—for a grown man or woman than to have urinary leakage; and sexual impotence is scarcely a minor matter. The defense is usually that the aftereffect was "an unavoidable complication." Is it asking too much of the doctor (in this most confidential and trusting of relationships) that if he claims these complications are *un*preventable, the patient be informed about their possibility *before* the procedure? Fortunately, most of our courts think that it is not and that the patient has every right to be informed.

Now to some specific cases involving diagnostic procedures.

Warren Asch, a man in his late forties, was suspected of having an abdominal ulcer. His physician, Dr. Benjamin Wolff, suggested he be admitted to the hospital for a work-up to determine what was causing his symptoms of abdominal pain. Mr. Asch had undergone the GI series and other tests, which were negative, when it was decided that an esophagoscopy be performed. The instrument to be used was of rigid metal; a light was attached to it, so that when it reached the esophagus, or gullet, by way of the mouth, the organ could be seen visually. In this procedure, which is usually done under local anesthesia, great care must be taken not to injure any tissue, especially the esophagus.

In this case, the instrument perforated the patient's esophagus and caused an abnormal opening in his chest. As a result, a serious condition known as "mediastinitis" developed. For a while the patient was actually on the verge of death, and though he eventually recovered, it was with permanent damage.

The defense in the action was that the doctor did nothing wrong. Unfortunately for the patient, mediastinitis was one of the risks or hazards of the procedure, which could occur even in the "best" of hands in a small percentage of cases.

The cross-examination of the doctor was rather revealing. I present it at some length, without comment, so that you can draw your own conclusions:

Q. Doctor, as I understand your answer on direct examination, when doing an esophagoscopy a perforation of the esophagus is one of the risks of the procedure that can occur even though the doctor is careful?

A. That's correct.

Q. What you are saying then, is that the perforation which occurred in this case was an unavoidable accident for which you are completely blameless.

A. That's right.

Q. Doctor, where the perforation extends beyond the esophagus into the chest cavity and mediastinitis develops, as in this case, that is a serious condition and constitutes a threat to the life of the patient?

A. That's true.

Q. That being so, did you advise the patient beforehand that this procedure, which was merely for diagnostic purposes, carried with it such a dangerous risk?

A. No, I did not.

Q. Do you agree that in inserting the scope and directing it through the gullet, care has to be taken not to use too much force?

A. Yes.

Q. Because if too much force is used, it may perforate the esophagus?

A. True.

Q. Would you agree then that it would be a departure from good medical practice for a doctor to use too much force.

A. Yes. I suppose that's true.

Q. Doctor, do you know how much pressure must be exerted on the esophagus before it will tear or rupture?

A. I do not.

Q. It's true, is it not, that the esophagus itself is rather strong because it is lined by a vascular membrane, reinforced by a layer of muscle, and has a tough fibrous covering?

A. Yes.

Q. And in order to perforate the esophagus to the extent that the mediastinum becomes involved, *more force* would have to be used than necessary.

A. No, that's not so.

Q. Doctor, you are no doubt familiar with the authoritative work of John D. Kernan, "Perforation of Esophagus as a Surgical Emergency," which appears in the *Surgical Clinics of North America*, issue of April, 1950?

A. I am.

Q. Do you agree with this statement at page 405 of that authoritative work, "Only the actual penetration of the muscular and fibrous layers of the wall (of the esophagus) permit leakage into the mediastinum. To accomplish such a rupture, it has been shown experimentally that a pressure of 5 to 10 pounds per square inch must be developed; *far more than should be used* in any intra-esophagus procedure"?

A. I do not.

Q. Doctor, do you agree with this statement in the February 1951 issue of the *Surgical Clinics of North America*, "These mishaps will seldom occur in a *carefully* performed endoscopic examination"?

A. No, I do not.

Q. Doctor, you are also no doubt familiar with the authoritative volumes of work entitled, *Practice of Medicine* by Frederick Tice?

A. Of course.

Q. I have volume 7, at page 119 which deals with esophagoscopy. Let me ask you if you agree with this statement, "The dangers and complications are few in the hands of the trained. When an attempt is made to pass the instrument without direct vision of the lumen (opening) or *where undue pressure is exerted on passing it too rapidly*, perforation of the walls of the esophagus may result"?

A. No.

Q. Doctor, the last medical authority I am going to ask you about is by the man who invented the scope, Dr. Chevalier Jackson. His book *Bronchoesophagology* is a classic in this field of medicine.

A. That's true.

Q. Doctor, do you agree with this statement at page 234, "The esophagoscope must await the opening of these tonically closed points while it is continuously but gently pressed in exactly the proper place. The gates must not be 'crashed.' For him who tries to crash it, the crico-pharangeal gate is literally a 'Gate of Tears.'"

A. Yes. I suppose that's correct.

Q. Doctor, the last question with which I will trouble you, is to ask you whether you agree with this statement by Dr. Jackson at page 242, "Complications after esophagoscopy are to be avoided in large measure by the exercise of gentleness, care and the skill that is acquired by practice. If the instructions herein given are followed, esophagoscopy is *practically* without mortality"?

A. No, I do not agree.

The last case in this section concerns a diagnostic procedure known as *cardiac catheterization.* A long plastic tube, the catheter, is inserted into the vein of an arm or leg, under local anesthesia, and passed into the chambers of the heart. The tube contains a contrast medium so that X rays can be taken and various other tests and studies made, all of which are designed to help determine more precisely the nature of a coronary defect. Since there is usually evidence of a reaction— at which time the procedure can, and should, be *terminated*— there is very little risk of a fatality occurring.

Alexandra Hoffert had been born with a heart defect, a murmur. It gave her very little trouble, and other than avoiding excessive physical activity, she led a normal life. She married when she was nineteen years old, and at twenty had her first child; no complications developed during her pregnancy or during delivery. But at the end of her second pregnancy she developed palpitations of the heart just before going into labor. Her doctor suggested that she have a heart checkup to see if she was a candidate for heart surgery, and referred her to Dr. George McBribe who specialized in the diagnosis of heart problems and who was qualified to do cardiac catheterization.

Dr. McBribe did various tests and studies in his office, but for the purpose of the cardiac catheterization she was admitted to a hospital. She and her husband had been told that there was minimal danger connected with the procedure, and therefore she walked cheerfully to the hospital. Two days later she was taken to the Cardiac Research Laboratory where the procedure was done.

Her condition at the outset was good. Her blood pressure was 110/80 (normal) and her pulse was about 90 (also normal).

The heart is a complicated little machine consisting of four chambers. There are the right atrium and the right ventricle, which receives impure blood from the veins and pumps it over to the lungs to be oxygenated; then the pure blood surges to the left atrium and then to the left ventricle, where it is pumped out to the aorta and from there to even the smallest toe.

During the procedure being performed on Mrs. Hoffert, a severe reaction known as nodal tachycardia developed when the catheter reached the right atrium. Her heartbeat jumped from a normal of 90 to an abnormal 170 per minute.

Dr. McBribe immediately withdrew the catheter. He waited ten minutes and then gave the patient some medication to bring her heart rate back to normal. This was not successful, so he gave her a second dose. After an hour of nodal rhythm, the heart reverted to a normal sinus rhythm. But the heart rhythm did not return to its normal of 90 but remained at 120. It is important to note that the normal heartbeat is between 60 and 100 per minute; anything above that is abnormal, and is called tachycardia.

After having waited a total of almost two hours from the time the patient first developed complications, Dr. McBribe decided to *resume* the procedure even though she was still in tachycardia—her heartbeat still abnormally fast at 120.

What happened next was inevitable, except that this time when the patient developed ventricular tachycardia she went into ventricular fibrillation (heart out of control). Mrs. Hoffert was dead in a matter of minutes.

In my search through the medical literature dealing with

cardiac catheterization and its complications, I came upon a report written eight years before the patient's death by a special committee headed by Dr. André Cournand, the leading authority on the subject. It said that in order to prevent serious complications, "any complaint of a queer or unusual feeling of the patient, a *significant increase in heart rate*, evidence of vagal stimulation, *persistence of induced premature ventricular contractions*, or right bundle branch block, should lead without delay to *termination* of the procedure."

Had the doctor heeded those words; had he counted his blessings when he did not lose the patient the first time she had gone into nodal tachycardia; had he *terminated* the procedure instead of resuming it again; had he . . .

But he didn't.

V

DOOMED TO DIE?

*A diagnostic procedure—an injection of dye
into the urinary tract results in severe
complications and death*

Albert Wesley could not believe that his wife, Rose, was dead. "It can't be true. It can't be true," he repeated over and over again. "All she had was some pain in her back, and she just went into the hospital to have a checkup. What about the children? Who will take care of them?"

It couldn't be true. But it was. Rose Wesley had died on Wednesday, December 10th, at the Hackleford Hospital. She was forty-two years old.

A few days before her untimely death, Mrs. Wesley had felt some pain in her back, enough pain for her to forego her usual Monday-morning trip to church to make a novena, and to go instead to her family doctor, Warren Manheim. After Dr. Manheim examined Mrs. Wesley, he suggested that she go into the hospital for a "urological work-up" under the care of a urologist, Dr. Miles Bertram. She followed this recommendation, and on Tuesday entered the Hackleford Hospital to have

67

X rays taken of her kidneys and urinary system. This procedure is called an "intravenous pyelogram" (IVP), and is performed by first injecting a contrast medium or dye into a vein and then taking a series of X rays. It is a diagnostic procedure, similar to a GI-series study of the stomach, in which barium is used as the contrast medium.

The following day Rose was wheeled into the X-ray room, and at 1:05 P.M. a resident, Dr. Victor Favali, with the assistance of an X-ray technician, began the procedure. First he did a "skin test" to determine whether or not the patient was allergic to Diodrast, the dye to be used to create the contrast medium for the X ray. He injected 1 cc into a vein in her arm, and waited about one-half hour to see if any reaction would develop, such as redness or swelling. Seeing no "adverse reaction," Dr. Favali proceeded to inject the full quantity of about 20 cc's of Diodrast. But he had injected only 5 cc's (about one teaspoonful) in about five minutes, when he suddenly noticed that Mrs. Wesley was having a "peculiar" reaction.

The patient complained of "shortness of breath," and her skin had become "flushed." The IVP was immediately discontinued, and when Mrs. Wesley started to have "convulsions" Dr. Favali gave her an injection of adrenalin (a heart stimulant). He *ordered* oxygen. The family doctor, Manheim, was notified by phone at 1:45 P.M., and he advised that Mrs. Wesley be treated for the allergic reaction by being given cortisone and adrenalin.

Dr. Manheim arrived at the hospital about forty-five minutes later and was told that Dr. Walter Michaels (an assistant to the urologist, Dr. Bertram) had seen the patient and had *countermanded* his orders of adrenalin and cortisone because he saw no evidence of allergic reaction. Instead, Dr. Michaels thought that the patient had a "cerebral hemorrhage." Dr. Manheim, after checking the patient, saw no evidence of cerebral vascular accident, and reinstituted the treatment for allergic reaction.

At 3:40 P.M., within two hours after the procedure had begun, Rose Wesley was dead.

The next day, an autopsy was performed by the Medical Examiner of the City of New York. The report that was issued gave the cause of death as: "Shock following intravenous Diodrast for diagnostic pyelogram (renal) left pylonephosis (localized) coronary sclerosis."

Rose Wesley left two children, Samuel, fifteen, and Margaret, eleven. Until the time of her death, Rose had been in excellent health. Besides working as a beautician three days a week, she took care of a six-room apartment, did all the family shopping, cooking, and cleaning, and made the children their clothes; she was a whiz at the sewing machine.

When he heard of his wife's death, Albert Wesley was shocked. She had walked into the Hackleford Hospital for what seemed routine tests; a day later she was carried out dead. Mr. Wesley had tried to question the doctors, but all they would say was: "It happens. She was allergic; no one is to blame."

Albert decided to consult a lawyer. He could not believe that his wife's death could have been that innocent. Irving Rosenkrantz, whom he went to see, decided to investigate the facts. First the attorney obtained a copy of the Hackleford Hospital records, and the Medical Examiner's report. They revealed most of the facts that have been set forth, but after consultation with some doctors the attorney decided to take the case.

An action was started shortly thereafter against the following defendants:

1. John Waverly and Alice Mills, copartners doing business as the Hackleford Hospital;

2. Dr. Victor Favali, the resident physician;

3. Dr. Warren Manheim, the family doctor;

4. the estate of Miles Bertram, the urologist (who happened to die shortly after Mrs. Wesley);

5. Dr. Walter Michaels, the assistant urologist employed by Dr. Bertram.

Attorney Rosenkrantz handled all the preliminary procedures, including the taking of the examinations-before-trial of the various defendants. He did an excellent job. Shortly before the trial he consulted with my partner Hank Dillof, with whom I have been associated for over twenty years, and retained our firm to try the case.

The trial of the case came on before Mr. Justice Lawrence J. Peltin and a jury some time later; it lasted for seven days. James Dempsey was the attorney for the hospital and the resident, Dr. Favali. The attorney for Dr. Manheim and the assistant urologist, Dr. Michaels, was Desmond T. Barry. The reason for his appearing for both the family doctor and the assistant urologist was an unusual coincidence in that both carried their malpractice insurance with the same insurance company. The late William Richardson, of the firm of Martin, Clearwater and Bell, was the attorney for the urologist Dr. Bertram's estate. His firm are general counsel to the Medical Society of New York State, and are retained by its insurance company.

Choosing, a jury in *any* type of case is never an easy matter. This is especially true in the malpractice case. The public has the image of Ben Casey and Dr. Kildare as dedicated medical knights in shining armor. They must be made aware that the medical profession is *not* being attacked; that the term "malpractice" simply means the *negligence* of a person in his professional capacity, in a particular instance, whether he be a lawyer, engineer, accountant, or any person who deals with the public; and that neither the doctor's reputation nor right to practice medicine is involved in this case. The only issue for the jury to decide is, "Was the patient treated in the accepted and proper medical manner?" If the answer is "Yes," then that is the end of the plaintiff's case. If the answer is "No," then the plaintiff is entitled to recover, and should be adequately compensated.

Since a doctor literally holds a patient's life in his hands, it is his duty to see to it that *every* safeguard and precaution is taken in the treatment so that the patient is not exposed to unnecessary risks and complications. "First, no harm to the patient"—this credo must be stressed over and over again.

In my opening remarks to the jury, I pinpointed our claim by enumerating the charge of malpractice or negligence as follows:

Concerning the hospital and its resident, Dr. Favali:

1. Dr. Favali was inexperienced. He had performed only three or four IVP procedures, and had never had any special training in how to do them or how to treat a patient who develops an allergic reaction to the drug;

2. The hospital did not have the proper equipment *immediately* available to treat an adverse reaction—particularly oxygen and certain necessary drugs.

As to Dr. Michaels, the assistant urologist, he was negligent because:

1. He failed to recognize that the patient was suffering from an allergic reaction, and mistakenly thought it was a cerebral hemorrhage;

2. he improperly *countermanded* the orders of the family doctor that Mrs. Wesley be treated for allergic reaction;

3. he left the patient while she was critically ill, and before the family doctor had arrived.

James Dempsey, attorney for the hospital and the resident, in his opening remarks told the jury that Hackleford Hospital is an approved and accredited hospital, that Dr. Favali was properly trained and had properly injected the Diodrast—which has been used "millions of times" without complications—and that when the patient showed signs of a reaction he did everything that could be done. "In fact," the attorney urged, "we will prove to you that this lady was in oxygen within *one* or *two* minutes after this allergic reaction became manifest."

Desmond Barry, the attorney for Dr. Manheim and Dr. Michaels, had to straddle a wide road when he stated that "neither doctor had done anything wrong," that it was all very sad, very unfortunate, but Mrs. Wesley was a "one in a million" case—and no one was to blame. In fact, he took the interesting position that once the complications had begun she was such a seriously sick woman that *nothing* could have been done to save her. He put it this way:

"Once the dye was started, once the Diodrast was put in, *that was the end.* I think there will be testimony here, gentlemen, that *nothing* could have been done to save that lady once she received this injection."

William Richardson, in his opening, simply took the position that his client, Dr. Bertram, had nothing to do with giving the injection or in treating any complications that developed. (Of course, he had ignored completely the responsibility of Dr. Bertram for the negligent acts of his employee, Dr. Michaels—if the latter was found to have been at fault.)

The jury listened to each lawyer with great interest. The nature of the tragedy, responsibility for which they were to decide, caught their imagination. They hung on every word.

The lines of battle were drawn: it now remained for the presentation of the proof to decide whether the death of Mrs. Wesley was an unavoidable "one in a million" case, or whether all or some of the defendants were guilty of negligence as charged.

The first witnesses to be called to the stand were the husband and two children of Rose Wesley. They testified as to her previous general good health, and detailed her activities both as a wife and mother.

A very effective witness was the daughter, Margaret, who

had been eleven years old when her mother died and was now sixteen. She was still going to school, but now had taken complete responsibility for the shopping and cooking and other activities necessary for the care of her father and brother. The last question she was asked had a profound effect on the jury:

> Q. Who takes care of you now?
> A. *Me.*

Prior to the trial itself, each of the defendants had been questioned under oath as to what, precisely, had been done for Mrs. Wesley—their findings, treatment, and so forth. This "examination-before-trial" may be used at the trial as evidence by the party that takes the deposition. At this trial, the testimony of all the defendants was read to the jury. It represented their version of what had taken place and was the basis on which our experts could testify as to whether there was malpractice or not.

As our first expert witness, we called Dr. Frank Samuels, a urologist who testified that Mrs. Wesley had *not* been treated in the accepted and proper manner in that she should have been promptly treated for the allergic reaction and not for a cerebral hemorrhage.

The hospital's attorney, James Dempsey, effectively cross-examined the witness by showing that an adverse reaction *can* occur with no one to blame and that Mrs. Wesley *was* given proper medication to counteract it in the form of antihistamines, barbiturates, and oxygen. His last question was:

> Q. And, Doctor, do you know from your experience over the years that where a person does get a sensitivity reaction to this, or other substances, that despite the very best efforts of all the doctors, the patient sometimes succumbs? Do you know that, sir?
> A. Yes.

Dr. Samuels had been a great disappointment to our case. His testimony failed to carry any conviction. He had agreed with almost everything the defense attorneys asked him, and at the end of his testimony our case had begun to look quite bleak.

But fortunately we had a second expert in reserve, Dr. Israel Beyers, a surgeon with fine qualifications.

Dr. Beyers testified that the resident, Dr. Favali, who had done this procedure only three or four times prior to his treatment of Mrs. Wesley, was *not* experienced enough to do this procedure without being supervised. At the very least, he testified, there should have been an experienced doctor present at the time to see to it that everything was done properly, a doctor who would have been able to cope with any adverse reaction. Our expert was also critical of the fact that oxygen was not immediately available to treat any reaction: it should have been present "in the room," not merely available elsewhere in the hospital.

As for Dr. Michaels, the witness said he was guilty of malpractice on two counts. First, since this was an obvious allergic reaction to the Diodrast, it was wrong of Dr. Michaels to have countermanded the orders given by Dr. Manheim. Second, Dr. Michaels should not, under any circumstances, have left the patient while she was still critically ill.

Dr. Beyers was also critical of the fact that the patient had been given an injection of Sodium Luminal, a "long-acting" barbiturate. She should have been given a "short-acting" barbiturate such as Sodium Pentothal. He explained that the literature put out by the manufacturers of the drug specifically states that if convulsions should develop, a *short-acting* drug should be given intravenously. The reason for this, Dr. Beyers went on to explain, was as follows:

> You don't want the long-acting barbiturate because it keeps the patients depressed and keeps them unconscious.

They cannot react adequately for a long period of time. With a short-acting, which is mainly used for the control of the convulsions, you can then get control of the patient adequately because they become conscious and they can react and cooperate with a doctor at that particular time.

Unlike the cross-examination of Dr. Samuels, that which was directed to Dr. Beyers proved to be ineffective. He held firmly to his position that there had indeed been malpractice. Though the defense kept pressing their point that once a severe reaction to the drug occurs there is very little that can be done for the patient, with death an "inevitable" result, Dr. Beyers held to the contrary position. Witness his firmness under the cross-examination by Mr. Barry:

Q. Now, let me go back to this, Doctor—do I interpret your testimony, in substance, as saying that with the proper equipment in the hospital and the proper measures taken by any doctor that was in attendance upon that patient or this patient, any of the nurses, that death was— that death would have been avoided?

A. Yes, sir; yes, sir.

Q. In other words, Doctor, do you recognize the probability risk or the risk inherent in this type of procedure?

A. Yes, I am taking full cognizance of it.

Q. You say, do you, that the risk can be avoided?

A. You can't avoid the risk, but you can avoid the death; if the proper test is done, you know what to do. When the reaction occurs and the proper treatment is done, the chances of survival are great.

Q. Well, we are going to come to that. You say the chances of survival are great. What percentage?

A. *I would say that at least 75 per cent of those patients with severe reactions, with the convulsions, can recover if treated properly.*

After Dr. Beyers's testimony, which completed our presentation, we rested. Our case was in. The defense lawyers at once made motions to dismiss the case on various grounds, but essentially because, they claimed, the plaintiff "had failed to establish any malpractice." Judge Peltin listened patiently to the three defense lawyers make their detailed argument, but denied their motions, saying in effect that "there were questions of fact to be decided by the jury."

The defense was now put to its proof, and since the first-named defendants were the Hackleford Hospital, Mr. Dempsey called as his first witness Mrs. Alice Mills, one of the owners of the hospital and the Hospital Administrator.

Mrs. Mills testified that Dr. Favali had come to the hospital one month before he performed the IVP on Mrs. Wesley as a "foreign resident." She said that the oxygen tank was kept in an alcove *right outside* the X-ray room, which was on the second floor of the hospital. On the day the procedure was done she received an emergency call and ran up to the X-ray room. When she arrived, the patient was *already* getting oxygen. She remained with the patient until she died several hours later.

Mrs. Mills was then asked about the "Oxygen Record Card," which showed 2:00 P.M. as the time when oxygen was started (the emergency occurred at 1:20 P.M.); she blithely explained, "Well, this simply means that at 2:00 P.M. we delivered *another* tank to the room." It was obvious that she had been well prepared for this question, and it was imperative that her veracity be attacked quickly.

After establishing that Mrs. Mills and Dr. Waverly, her husband, were in fact the owners of the Hackleford Hospital, I questioned her pointedly about the resident, Dr. Favali. It was shown that under the Certificate of Validity, which permitted the doctor to practice in New York State, there was the provision that "Practice in proprietory (private) hospitals must be under *supervision* of physician employed full time in residency and licensed in New York State."

   Q. Now, who is the physician under whose supervision he was that was in full-time residence at the hospital?
   A. At that time?
   Q. At that time.
   A. Dr. Rausch and Dr. Xylas.
   Q. Did they *supervise* the intravenous pyelogram procedure that Dr. Favali was performing?
   A. *They did not.*

Having shown that this was her private hospital, and that Dr. Favali as a "foreign resident" could practice only "under supervision" and that when this procedure was done on Mrs. Wesley, he was *not* supervised, we then proceeded to the question about the oxygen tank and when given.

   Q. Was there an oxygen tank in the room where the IVP procedure was performed?
   A. There was not.
   Q. Do you know that Dr. Favali in his sworn testimony, which is in evidence in this case, says, "Q. When did you start giving oxygen? A. As soon as we got the machine from *upstairs*—one minute or two minutes." Isn't it a fact that the oxygen tank was *upstairs* and not in an alcove outside the X-ray room?
   A. It could not have been upstairs.
   Q. Well, was it downstairs in the basement where you got the other cylinder?
   A. No, sir.
   Q. All right. Now, when oxygen is given a patient, a record is made, is there not, on a form called the Oxygen Record Card?
   A. Only when they are to receive continuous oxygen, never for short periods.

Q. Well, when you start giving a person oxygen, Mrs. Mills, at the beginning, does anybody know whether it is for a short period or a long period?

A. I am not talking about anybody in bed. I am talking about a patient in a recovery room or in X-ray or in the operating room for resuscitation. We never have a record on that type of a sheet.

Q. Well, it is your testimony, then, that the reason this card is filled out showing 2 P.M. is that that's when you started to get a second tank?

A. That is correct.

Q. Well, when you change a patient from one tank to another, don't you make a record of the fact that there has been a change from one tank to another, as long as you have got a card called—

A. No we do not.

Q. You say then, Mrs. Mills, that you don't record on your Oxygen Record Card the fact that this lady had been getting oxygen for some period of time before you made the change; is that what you are saying?

A. Not on that record.

Q. Well, on any record?

A. Yes, on the nurse's notes.

Q. Show it to me. *(The record is handed to witness.)*

A. On Dr. Favali's note. I am sorry.

Q. Show it to me.

A. "I asked the X-ray technician to hand me the prepared adrenalin, one to one thousand, while I was watching the patient who started having convulsions. One-half cc of adrenalin was given intravenously, slowly. Oxygen and airway *ordered* and Sodium Luminal, grains one and a half."

Q. Is that the entry you say is the one which shows that she had been getting oxygen and at two o'clock there was a change in the tanks?

A. This—

Q. Is that what you are saying Mrs. Mills?

A. Yes, sir.

Her testimony about the oxygen having been administered, as it should have been, *within a few minutes after the adverse reaction* of the patient, which was at 1:30 P.M., in the face of the Oxygen Record Card, which showed 2:00 P.M. as the start, was beginning to look shaky; but her testimony at this point became even weaker when she was asked about previous testimony she had given under oath at an examination-before-trial, three years earlier:

Q. Now, I ask you, Mrs. Mills, whether it isn't a fact that you were asked these questions and gave these answers under oath in February of 1960, a little over three years ago. "Q. During the time you were there, was any oxygen being given to her? A. I cannot recall. I must refer to the records." Do you remember being asked that question and giving that answer?

A. I don't recall that. All I know is that if it states that, then I agree that this is the answer I gave because I have reviewed that statement.

THE COURT. Is there any question, gentlemen, that that answer was given?

MR. DEMPSEY. No question at all, your Honor.

Q. Next question. Do you remember being asked this question and giving this answer: "Q. Will your record indicate when any oxygen was administered while you were there? A. Yes. It is stated here that oxygen was ordered." Do you remember being asked that question and giving that answer?

A. Yes.

Q. Now, this is the last question I am going to ask you about which you gave under oath at this time, and I am

going to ask you whether you remember being asked this
question and giving this answer: "Q. After looking at
those records is your own recollection refreshed as to
whether or not oxygen was administered while you were
in the X-ray room with Mrs. Wesley? A. *I cannot remember.*" Did you give that answer?

A. I most likely said it, and if it is written, this is what
I said.

The second witness called by Mr. Dempsey was Mrs. Mary
Brodkorp, who had been in charge of the X-ray Department
at the Hackleford Hospital while the procedure was done on
Mrs. Wesley. She testified that she had assisted Dr. Favali
in doing the IVP, and that when the patient started to get
convulsions she was immediately treated with medication and
"oxygen." She stated that the oxygen tank had been right
outside the door and had arrived in a few minutes.

The testimony of this witness seemed too pat, too well re-
hearsed, so I decided to test her memory on cross-examination.
There was a surprising payoff:

Q. You are an X-ray technician—is that correct, Mrs.
Brodkorp?
A. Yes.
Q. You are not a physician, are you?
A. No.
Q. And the X-ray room that we are talking about back
in December of 1958, at the Hackleford Hospital, where
this pyelogram was done, where was that located in the
hospital?
A. In the *basement* of the hospital.
Q. Has it always been in the basement?
A. Not always. When I started in the hospital it was
on the second floor.
Q. In any event, there is no question in your mind that

at the time of December of 1958, the pyelogram that was being done on Mrs. Wesley was being done in the X-ray room in the basement?

A. Oh, surely. This I know for sure.

THE COURT. No question about it. It was in the basement?

THE WITNESS. Sure.

THE COURT. It wasn't up on the second floor?

THE WITNESS. No.

As it developed from other proof produced by the hospital, this witness was in obvious error about where the X-ray room was at the time of the IVP, and so they found themselves in the embarrassing position of having to recall her to the witness stand later in the case, to admit her mistake. Her error cast a long shadow on her testimony about the oxygen tank being outside the door—in the "basement."

The next witness called by the hospital was Miss Fern Loring, who had been employed as assistant X-ray technician and was present at the time the IVP was done. She supported the claim that the oxygen was in the alcove outside the door of the X-ray room and was immediately given to the patient.

Her testimony had an artificial quality to it. Under the classical cross-examination approach as to whether she had discussed the case with anyone before taking the stand, her story became highly doubtful. For some reason witnesses are reluctant to admit they discussed the case with the attorney before coming to court. Since there is nothing improper in such a discussion, it is most unlikely that it did not take place. Miss Loring's insistence, even when questioned by the court, that she had *not* discussed it, cast doubt upon her testimony.

The hospital called as its next witness, its Director of Nursing, Mrs. Grace Bloom. This witness testified that she had got to the X-ray room about fifteen minutes after the complications had developed and that the patient was already receiving oxygen. She said that she had sent for a second tank, and then volunteered the information that "There is no record if you are just giving a little to a patient."

I decided to probe for more information about the oxygen tanks in my cross-examination of Mrs. Bloom:

Q. Do you know approximately how many cubic liters of oxygen are contained in a tank like that?

A. I believe there is 1,000.

Q. And in time, approximately how long, assume you start with a tank filled with 1,000 cubic liters of oxygen; in running time, about how long would it take to use up a tank like that?

A. At a normal rate of 6 liters, approximately 24 to 36 hours. According to the amount of liters you must give.

Q. Well, what was the rate of speed of the liters that Mrs. Wesley was receiving?

A. Well, you would start it off at 9 to 10. But you wouldn't keep it at 9 to 10. You would lower it then.

Q. The average use of it.

A. The average use of it, I would say at least 24, 36 hours.

Q. And does the tank have a gauge on it to indicate the number of liters left in the tank?

A. Yes, sir.

Q. In other words, so that you in the hospital and those that use the tank know when a tank is empty or when it is getting near empty, the gauge would indicate it?

A. That's right.

Q. Now, you tell his Honor and the jury how long did the first tank remain on Mrs. Wesley before it became empty and you had to get a second tank?

A. If you asked me the exact time, at the time I was not watching the time sir, and I would not know.

Q. All right. That is fair, Mrs. Bloom. I'm not going

to ask you the exact time. You give us the approximate
time that you say this first tank remained on Mrs. Wesley
when it ran out empty and it had to be replaced by a
second tank?

A. *All I know is that a second tank was brought in.
What time, I don't know.*

The best of the defense was yet to come.

They had assembled a battery of distinguished doctors, and
led off with Dr. Max Harnack, the foremost authority on con-
trast-media technique in the country. The mere recitation of
the articles and books he had written on the subject took over
one hour, and his personal use of Diodrast as a contrast medium included having given "some eight or nine thousand
injections."

When asked to assume the facts as reported in the hospital
record and autopsy findings, the doctor testified that everything had been done for Mrs. Wesley in accordance with good
hospital and medical practice and that it was common for any
resident, even an inexperienced one, to do the procedure. He
attributed Mrs. Wesley's death to a "one in a million" tragedy
that can occur with no one at fault.

The jury was obviously impressed with Dr. Harnack. His
excellent demeanor, coupled with the fact that he was *the*
authority, made it clear that unless his testimony could be
shaken on cross-examination the plaintiff's case was in serious
jeopardy.

Long before the trial I had read many of the articles written
by the doctor, but I had never anticipated that he would be
produced as a defense witness. The moment of truth, quite
literally, had arrived. How should this all-important witness
be handled?

I first developed from the doctor that the preliminary tests
(which are performed to determine if the patient is allergic
to Diodrast) are of little or no value. In fact, the tests may

be negative (as in this case) and yet the patient may still have a serious reaction.

Dr. Harnack agreed.

From this point I moved in to show that *since* the tests are of no value in foretelling whether the patient will have an allergic reaction (which might result in death), the physician performing the procedure should be an "experienced" physician qualified to treat any such complication.

The questioning, which proved to be highly enlightening, went as follows:

> Q. Now, Doctor, since the tests, the sensitivity tests and especially the skin test, this intradermal test that was done here, is of no value in determining whether a patient who is undergoing an intravenous pyelogram will or will not get an allergic reaction, isn't it essential that the person performing the procedure be not merely a physician but an *experienced* physician? Isn't that true, Doctor?
>
> A. No, it isn't.
>
> Q. I'm reading to you again, Doctor, from this article that you and your colleagues wrote in the *Journal of Radiology*, in July, or July to December of 1958. And I want to ask you whether this statement that you wrote in this article was true when you wrote it: "The injection should be made under the supervision of an *experienced* physician who has personally evaluated the patient and his history." Did you say that in your article, Doctor, and did you use the words "experienced physician"?
>
> A. Yes, I did. But you didn't read the title of the paper. I was talking about *angiocardiography*.

The doctor tried to explain away his use of the words "experienced physician" by saying the article I had read from did not deal with an IVP, but rather the contrast media used in the study of the heart. It turned out he was wrong. After further probing, he very meekly admitted his error.

Q. Dr. Harnack, in this article you weren't just dealing with angiography. Your article was dealing with reactions to iodide compounds used in any one of the different types of procedure, whether it is angiography, *pyelography*, venography, or any of the other procedures. Didn't you say that in your article here?

A. Yes.

Q. So that the statement you made before that this article is limited to angiography, that wasn't correct, was it?

A. Well, it includes it.

Q. Includes what?

A. Angiocardiography.

Q. What?

A. It includes angiocardiography. That is my chief concern.

Q. Didn't it also include *pyelography?*

A. It is the same substance, yes. *We included the whole field.*

At this point, an exceptionally interesting exchange took place:

Q. In other words, since the tests are of no real value, and untoward reactions may occur, the doctor who is doing the test should be in a position, know enough, and be experienced enough to know how to evaluate the untoward reaction, and more than be able to evaluate it, also know how to treat it. Isn't that true, Doctor?

A. May I answer that a little bit differently? In a hospital we assume that the lowliest intern has the chance to ask for help. So we let him do it. We know if he is in trouble he will call for help and help will come right away.

THE COURT. Suppose there is no help present, there is no other doctor around.

MR. DEMPSEY. I must object to that, if your Honor please.

THE COURT. Assume there is no help present. Let us assume there is no help present and no other doctors around.

MR. DEMPSEY. I must object, if your Honor pleases, to your Honor's question.

THE COURT. Objection overruled.

THE WITNESS. Well, I think he is in a predicament. This is what happens in your office. He does the best he can.

Q. Well, Doctor, if it is done in your office, we will assume that the man who does this procedure in the office is qualified to handle an untoward reaction, to recognize it and to know how to treat it. Isn't that the basis if a patient comes to you or to any urologist or any doctor for an intravenous pyelogram, is it unreasonable to say that the doctor who performs the procedure is qualified to recognize an untoward reaction, and also qualified to know how to treat it? Isn't that a fair basis?

A. Yes, sir.

Q. Now, you are assuming that if the resident doesn't know how to recognize it, and doesn't know how to treat it, he will be able to get help. That is your assumption?

A. Yes, sir.

Q. But if, on the other hand, help isn't around for one reason or another, not so much he is in trouble *but the patient is in trouble;* isn't that true, Dr. Harnack?

A. Yes, sir.

With the admission that it is not so much the doctor who is in trouble if he doesn't know how to treat the complication and there is no one around to help him (as in this case), but *the patient* who is in trouble, the plaintiff's case began to look much stronger. It was obvious that we had scored heavily through this noted authority's admission.

The last issue that remained to be developed through Dr. Harnack was that the complication *had to be immediately detected* and then treated promptly—and if done so, death *rarely* occurred. This was an important point, and if, out of Dr. Harnack's broad and respected experience and scholarship, this could be shown it would mean a great deal to our case.

Q. Isn't it true, Doctor, that time is of the essence; that where you get an untoward reaction, especially if it is a serious reaction, it must not only be immediately detected but it must be treated promptly, otherwise there may be a fatality; isn't that true, Dr. Harnack?

A. Yes, I agree.

Q. Now, insofar as your own experience, in your own hospital, hasn't it been your experience in your hospital, where you've got the right equipment, that fatalities are *rare* following an intravenous pyelogram?

A. They are rare, yes.

Q. Isn't it a fact, Doctor, didn't you in your article report that in the last *ten years*, at the New City Hospital, where you are connected, and did this survey, you did not have one fatality following an intravenous pyelogram? Isn't that true?

A. No. I think we had two in that list. In that table there are two deaths in 70,000.

Q. Two deaths in 70,000. We will get to that in a moment. I'm asking you whether it isn't a fact that in the last ten years you haven't had one fatality in an institution where it is done properly.

A. You are talking about in my own hands?

Q. I'm talking in your own experience.

A. In what year? 1963?

Q. Let me read to you, Doctor, from the article that you wrote: "Happily, in our experience, severe reactions

and fatalities have been rare. Only two deaths have occurred in more than 70,000 intravenous pyelographic
studies *and none within the past ten years.*" Did you say
that in this article which you published?

A. Yes, sir.

Q. No deaths in the last ten years, and only two in
some 70,000 intravenous pyelograms which were done
at the New City Hospital; is that right?

A. Yes, sir.

Q. And insofar as the two deaths that occurred, did
you say this? "Both fatalities were in elderly men, seriously ill." Is that the two cases of the 70,000 that died, in
both cases, number one, they were elderly individuals,
and number two, they were already seriously ill; isn't
that what you reported in this study?

A. Yes, sir. In 1958.

Dr. Harnack had proved to be a reluctant but wonderful
witness for the plaintiff. He established the following pertinent points:

1. that since the preliminary tests were of no value and
reactions may occur which would result in the patient's death,
the doctor doing the test should be "experienced";

2. that if a reaction occurs it must be promptly diagnosed
and promptly treated;

3. that if the above two factors take place, death rarely, if
ever, occurs.

The plaintiff's case was once again on the march, but there
were still more medical experts to be contended with.

The next witness was Dr. Rolfe Moore, a prominent Professor of Pathology. The defendants were bringing in all the
big guns. Dr. Moore testified that he had done over 25,000
autopsies and that once the patient develops convulsions he
is "doomed." Nothing after that can be done by way of treatment to save the patient.

The defendants were trying to have their cake and eat it.

Even if the patient *was* given the wrong treatment, since she immediately went into "convulsions," it made no difference because there was no way of reversing the hand of death.

Our first questions established that Dr. Moore's specialty was pathology and that he dealt primarily with autopsies on the dead. When asked if he had *ever* performed an intravenous pyelogram, he answered, "Never in my life."

Having first testified that convulsions were a *common* complication, Dr. Moore changed his answer to, "It is a very rare reaction."

He was then asked:

> Q. Well, Doctor, isn't it true, would you agree that where a person has had an allergic reaction and, say, had developed convulsions, that because it may have a fatal result that immediate, proper treatment must then be instituted?
>
> A. Of course.
>
> Q. Would you agree with that?
>
> A. Of course.
>
> Q. Isn't it conceivable that you may overcome the convulsions and reverse the downhill progress—isn't that true?
>
> A. By all means.

I could not resist asking Dr. Moore one final question: "When was the last time you ever *treated* a patient?" He gave a long, rambling discourse, which never answered the simple question that had been put to him. Some of the jurors started to titter before he was through. I doubt that Dr. Moore was much comfort to the defense.

On the same theme that Mrs. Wesley was "doomed to die" once convulsions had occurred, the defendants called Dr. Willard Stern, an internist and Professor of Medicine for over thirty years.

Dr. Stern testified that he had personally done over 500

IVP's, and that he had observed over 5,000. He stated that the patient's condition became "irreversible" immediately after the injection of 3 or 4 cc's of Diodrast and that from then on there was nothing that could possibly have prevented her death.

It was a story we had heard before.

But under cross-examination, Dr. Stern yielded to the crucible of truth. After a bit of fencing he admitted that "difficulty in breathing" and "convulsions" are *common* symptoms following the injection of Diodrast:

> Q. And you know, Doctor, that in the literature they tell you that where a person has gotten convulsions you treat them for the convulsions; isn't that true?
>
> A. That's right.
>
> Q. And I am asking you, Doctor, whether it isn't a fact that immediate proper treatment must be instituted, otherwise death may follow; isn't that true?
>
> A. Well, I think in selected cases your course is set.
>
> Q. Well, at the time, Doctor, is there any way of knowing what the course of a particular individual will be, whether or not he is a candidate for death or whether he is a candidate to survive, until the treatment is given that individual?
>
> A. I think when this patient had convulsions she had very little chance, if any, of living.
>
> Q. Well, Doctor, didn't we just agree that convulsions is one of the symptoms that is found following the injection of Diodrast?
>
> A. Convulsions and death. Yes, sir.
>
> Q. Well, Doctor, convulsions are usually secondary to asphyxia; isn't that true?
>
> A. Oh, I wouldn't say that.
>
> Q. Well, asphyxia is difficulty in breathing, isn't it?
>
> A. Yes.

Q. And when a person has difficulty in breathing, it is of the essence that he be given or get aid in the form of oxygen immediately—isn't that true?

A. Yes.

Dr. Stern did not know that in the two hours that Mrs. Wesley lived, the convulsions had stopped. When advised of this, he stated that it made no difference.

The last few questions asked of this medical expert had an astonishing ending:

Q. . . . are you saying to his Honor and the gentlemen of the jury that every patient, following the injection of Diodrast, that develops convulsions dies no matter what treatment is given to them? Is that what you are saying, Dr. Stern?

A. I think a large percent of them do, yes.

THE COURT. What is the answer?

THE WITNESS. I think a large percent of them do die.

THE COURT. Some percentage lives?

THE WITNESS. Possible.

Q. As a matter of fact, Dr. Stern, you really don't even know.

A. My experience with deaths with this dye is zero, sir. I don't know that question entirely.

Q. What do you mean by that answer, Doctor?

A. I've never seen a patient die with this injection of Diodrast.

Q. So that actually, Dr. Stern, you are in no position then to say that merely because she had some convulsions which, under medication, cleared up, that this lady therefore would have died no matter what treatment she had gotten—isn't that true, Dr. Stern?

A. *That's true.*

The defense now had but one more expert to call, Dr. Peter Cross, a urologist. He too joined the chorus that insisted Mrs. Wesley's condition was "irreversible," that she was in fact doomed.

In my cross-examination of this witness, I decided to put this issue to rest once for all. First, I sought his endorsement that, based on past experience, certain types of medication may be useful or helpful to overcome a particular symptom or problem. He agreed. Then, after establishing the authority of a particular article on the use of barbiturates, I questioned him further:

> Q. I want to ask you whether you agree with this statement, Doctor: "Usually restlessness, anxiety and confusion presage the untoward sequellae. *Convulsions* may develop at the same time. For these symptoms the barbiturates Seconal Sodium or pental sodium given intravenously *are* particularly useful." Do you agree with that statement, Doctor?
> A. I do.
> Q. In other words, then, when a patient has *convulsions*, there are medications, certain short-acting barbiturates, which are useful in the treatment of that symptom —isn't that true?
> A. That's true.

There still remained one more important witness for the defense, the *defendant* Dr. Walter Michaels.

Dr. Michaels had seen the patient a few minutes after the adverse reaction had developed, and diagnosed her condition as a "stroke" or cerebral hemorrhage. He testified that she was receiving oxygen when he arrived. He remained about twenty minutes, and waited until Dr. Manheim, the family doctor, arrived before he left.

Since we were convinced that Dr. Michaels was not telling

the truth on several counts, this would be an important cross-examination. We felt sure that he had made the wrong diagnosis of her condition in calling it a cerebral hemorrhage and not a reaction to the IVP; that he was wrong in countermanding the orders of Dr. Manheim to treat her for the reaction; that she was *not* getting oxygen while he was there; and finally that he left *before* Dr. Manheim arrived and not *when* he arrived, so that in the interval no qualified doctor was in attendance except the resident, Dr. Favali.

On the question of the oxygen he was asked:

Q. Doctor, would it be correct to say that you arrived in the X-ray room within a matter of a few minutes after some adverse reaction had taken place to Mrs. Wesley?

A. As far as I recollect, yes.

Q. And since it has been testified here that this adverse reaction occurred approximately 1:40–1:45 in the afternoon of that day, you arrived then within a matter of a few minutes after that?

A. Within a matter of a few minutes after Dr. Bertram asked me to run down and see the patient.

Q. All right. Now, you say that when you got there you saw Dr. Favali or somebody else giving her oxygen?

A. To the best of my recollection.

Q. Did you ever tell anybody, prior to the witness stand today, that to the best of your recollection, during all the time you were there in the X-ray room, she hadn't received any oxygen?

A. Not that I recall consciously.

Q. Well, now, you, too, Dr. Michaels, were examined, questioned under oath back in February 19th of 1960?

A. Yes, sir.

Q. Do you remember being asked this question, in 1960, and giving this answer? "Was any oxygen administered while you were there? A. Not to my recollection."

Do you remember being asked that question?

A. I do.

Q. Now, you tell his Honor and the gentlemen of the jury which answer is correct, the one you swore to in 1960 . . . or the testimony you are giving here on the witness stand.

A. To the best of my recollection, at the present time, oxygen was already being administered when I got there.

Q. Doctor, are you now saying then that when you said three years ago that she received no oxygen all the time you were there, that you were wrong?

A. I could have been wrong.

Q. Could you be wrong now?

A. Yes, I could be wrong now.

Concerning his diagnosis of "cerebral hemorrhage," the cross-examination went as follows:

Q. Now, am I correct in saying, Doctor, that aside from being told that she complained of flushing of the skin, or, as you said, of feeling funny, that Dr. Favali told you that she also complained of difficulty in breathing?

A. Must have been so then.

Q. And isn't a complaint of difficulty in breathing one of the common complications following an allergic reaction to Diodrast?

A. Yes.

Q. Now, then were you told by Dr. Favali that the lady went into convulsions?

A. That is correct.

Q. And isn't it true that convulsions is a common complication of allergic reaction to Diodrast?

A. One of the complications.

Q. Doctor, where a person has had a cerebral hemorrhage it means by that that there has been a rupture of blood vessels in the brain—isn't that true?

A. That is correct.

Q. And when an artery, say, bursts, the blood escapes into the brain.

A. Or outside the brain.

Q. Or outside the brain. And it is true, is it not, that where a person has had a cerebral hemorrhage, since the blood has now broken out or escaped from the artery or vein, that it results in a, at the beginning, in a lowering of the blood pressure; that's true, is it not?

A. Most frequently.

Q. Well, don't you know that Dr. Favali took the blood pressure of Mrs. Wesley immediately after she had the allergic reaction and reports that her blood pressure was 140/80?

A. Yes.

Q. That's normal, isn't it, Doctor?

THE COURT. Or within normal limits?

THE WITNESS. Well, 140/80 for a patient in that age group is certainly within normal limits. But I never knew what her blood pressure was before.

Q. Did you ask Dr. Favali if he had taken a blood pressure?

A. No, sir.

Q. Did you ask what the blood pressure was?

A. No, sir. Not that I recall.

Our cross-examination of this key witness was progressing satisfactorily, but we still had two more important issues to clarify. We next broached the problem of whether or not Dr. Michaels had indeed countermanded the orders of Dr. Manheim that she be treated for the reaction to the drug:

Q. Were you told that Dr. Manheim had ordered that she be given cortisone in addition to adrenalin, that she be treated for an allergic reaction?

A. I do not remember that.

Q. You don't remember that, Doctor?

A. No.

Q. Isn't it a fact that you countermanded the orders given by Dr. Manheim that she be treated for an allergic reaction?

A. I did not countermand any orders. I left my own orders for the treatment of the patient as I found her and as I interpreted the situation.

Q. But you say that as to what Dr. Manheim, what instructions he had given when he was called, you don't remember that?

A. I do not recall. No.

Q. All right.

A. *I can't say what he ordered.*

Now only one question remained: Had Dr. Michaels remained with Mrs. Wesley until her family physician arrived —or had he left her unattended, as claimed by the plaintiff? The cross-examination on this point was rather protracted, but it is so revealing that it is worth quoting at length.

Q. Did you see Dr. Manheim when he came into that X-ray room?

A. Yes.

Q. Did you talk to him?

A. Well, when Dr.—

Q. Did you talk to him, Doctor?

A. I'm trying to recollect. When Dr. Manheim came in, he took one look at what was happening and I don't recall exactly whether or not I had much to say to him, if anything at all. He took control of the case, which was rightfully his, and naturally, since I was not the physician of record, I withdrew and left the case in his charge.

MR. KRAMER. Your Honor, I move to strike that answer out as not responsive to the question I asked.

THE COURT. Strike it out. The jury is told to disregard it. Did Dr. Manheim arrive while you were there?

THE WITNESS. He arrived before I left, your Honor.

THE COURT. You saw him?

THE WITNESS. As far as I recollect. Yes, sir.

THE COURT. And then you left?

THE WITNESS. And then I left.

THE COURT. And you know who—you knew who Dr. Manheim was?

THE WITNESS. Yes. I know Dr. Manheim.

THE COURT. All right.

Q. Did you talk to him?

A. I don't remember. I don't remember whether or not I said anything to him. And if I said anything to him, what I said to him.

Q. As a matter of fact, Dr. Michaels, isn't it a fact that you left in anticipation of Dr. Manheim arriving? Isn't that the truth?

A. I do not recollect. As far as I can recall, I waited until Dr. Manheim arrived in the hospital to take control of the case.

Q. Well, now, Doctor, I'm going to refresh your memory.

THE COURT. Wait a minute. By that do you mean this, Doctor, in plain language: That you cannot tell us now at the time you left whether Dr. Manheim had arrived or not?

THE WITNESS. To the best of my recollection, Judge, I saw Dr. Manheim before I left.

THE COURT. All right.

Q. Now I'm going to see if I can't refresh your recollection, namely to the effect that you left in anticipation of Dr. Manheim arriving. Isn't that the truth?

A. I can't answer that.

Q. Back in this examination-before-trial, in February

of 1960, while under oath, do you remember being asked this question and giving this answer? "q. Will you be kind enough to tell us what examination you made? a. Well, when I walked into the X-ray room the patient was convulsing. I did a routine clinical neurological examination, namely knee jerks, ankle jerks, Babinski, and if I recall correctly, pupilary reaction, and which neurological findings were very uncommon. I made a tentative finding or diagnosis of cerebral hemorrhage and ordered some Sodium Luminal or sodium barbital to be given intramuscularly. And if I remember, I think I ordered also that an intravenous to be started on her. I do not recall exactly what I ordered. I made a note on the chart and *left in anticipation of Dr. Manheim's arrival at the hospital*." Were you asked that question and did you give that answer under oath in February of 1960?

a. If it is on that examination-before-trial, obviously it is the question and answer.

the court. Was it true when you gave that answer in 1960 on the examination-before-trial?

the witness. To the best of my recollection, your Honor.

It was now absolutely clear that Dr. Michaels had in fact left Mrs. Wesley, who was then in critical condition, in the hands of an inexperienced resident. Although Dr. Manheim, in his testimony, tried to protect Dr. Michaels by saying that the doctor was there when he arrived in the X-ray room, he finally had to admit that in the examination-before-trial he did *not* mention that Dr. Michaels was in fact present when he arrived at the hospital.

This was the posture of the case at the completion of all the testimony.

In the summations that followed, the defense attorneys reiterated their chant that "everything was properly done," "this was an unavoidable complication," "with development of convulsions she was *doomed to death*," and that "this is something that happens once in a million injections and no one is to blame."

But *was* this *really* so?

Fortunately, the jury did not think so. They were satisfied that there *was* negligence on the part of all the defendants except the family doctor, and rendered a verdict for Mr. Wesley and the two children that, with interest and costs, was in excess of $100,000.

VI

NOBODY CARED

*An obstetrical case—delivery of twins, followed
by death of the mother*

Just about everyone, at one
time or another, has been treated in the Emergency Room,
clinic, or ward of a municipal hospital. The kind of care you
got probably varied from good to bad—or perhaps to indif-
ferent. In New York City there are about twenty city-owned
and -operated hospitals. They have been—even in recent
months—the subject of criticism so sharp it has bordered on
the scandalous. In many instances the buildings themselves
are old and dilapidated, the equipment, for the most part,
inadequate, the nursing staff shorthanded and overworked,
and the medical staff far from the best. Lacking also, at times,
is a *sense of dedication.*

The case of Louisa Alvaro, a young woman of twenty-six,
is just such a story. Mrs. Alvaro was delivered of a normal
set of twins at a city hospital, but during the delivery she
began to hemorrhage. Afterward, she continued to bleed until, within fifteen hours, she died. We claimed her death was
unnecessary: it occurred because *nobody cared.*

100

Louisa Alvaro had met her husband, George, in their native Puerto Rico. They came to this country in 1951, married, and then had two children. Several years later Mrs. Alvaro was again pregnant, and on July 18, 1959, at 5:00 A.M., she was admitted to the city-owned Washington Hospital. Three hours later a resident delivered her of a set of twins. The newborn children were fine, but the mother had begun to bleed vaginally, a condition known as postpartum hemorrhage. By midnight of that same day she was dead.

At autopsy performed by a city pathologist found the cause of death to be "an acute fulminating massive liver necrosis" (destruction of the liver); it further stated that Mrs. Alvaro had had the condition long before she came to the hospital.

An action against the City of New York was brought by Mr. Alvaro in behalf of himself and the four children.

Seven years later, in 1965, the case came on for trial before Mr. Justice Nathaniel T. Helman and a jury. The case was defended by Jerry Wunder, an assistant Corporation Counsel with extensive knowledge and experience.

The opening statement made by each lawyer draws the lines of battle. It gives each side an opportunity to set forth its side of the story. There is the danger of overstating your case at this time or of providing the other side with detailed information about your claim so that they will be forewarned and forearmed. The element of surprise must be retained. It has been said that a good opening statement should be like a woman's dress: long enough to cover the subject, yet short enough to be interesting.

In my opening to the jury I outlined the principal facts of the case and the basis of our claim. I described how Mrs. Alvaro had lost 200 cc's of blood during the delivery (a pint is 500 cc's), and how, before she was moved to a stretcher, she had lost an additional 300 to 400 cc's of blood.

I advised the jury that it is not unusual for some bleeding

to take place after delivery, particularly of twins, but that anything more than 500 cc's is considered abnormal, and constitutes "hemorrhaging." We would show that at 3:00 P.M., Mrs. Alvaro had bled an additional 300 to 400 cc's, making a total of 1,000 cc's (about two pints), and that she then became jaundiced, and died about midnight.

Mrs. Alvaro had been given *some* blood transfusion and treatment, but not enough, I claimed. We would prove that what was given was too little and too late. "In short," I told the jury, "we charge the City with being responsible for her death. We say that had they exercised reasonable care in the treatment of Mrs. Alvaro, she would be alive today."

Mr. Wunder, in behalf of the city, then outlined the defense. He said that the proof would show that Mrs. Alvaro was cared for properly; that simply because there was a bad result the city was not necessarily to blame; that the autopsy showed she had extensive damage to her liver and that this condition existed *before* her admission to the hospital and that the hemorrhaging did not, in fact, have anything to do with her death, but rather that she had died because of the bad liver condition.

In the normal trial of a case, it is customary for the plaintiff to call his own witnesses first, rest his case, and then await the defense before he can cross-examine. The malpractice case is somewhat different, and experience has taught me that it is sometimes more effective to call the defendant or the defendant's employees as your own witnesses. While this provides definite limits to your questioning of the witness, it does have the advantage of catching the defense off guard, and denies them the opportunity of coming in with prepared answers to your charges.

In this case, I had to decide whether to offer the hospital record in evidence, then call my medical expert and have him explain where the negligence had occurred, or whether to subpoena a doctor on the staff of the hospital as my own witness. I elected to do the latter.

As one of my first witnesses, I therefore called Dr. Alan Rhenston to the stand. He was the assistant resident of obstetrics at Washington Hospital, and had assisted in the care of Mrs. Alvaro; at the time of the trial Dr. Rhenston was a practicing obstetrician and gynecologist. He did not relish being subpoenaed to court, and proved to be a most reluctant witness.

Anyone who graduates from a recognized medical school is eligible to take the State Board of Regents examination, and if he passes that he has become a qualified doctor. But after the exam, the doctor is obliged to serve an "internship" for one year, and subsequently, if he wants to specialize in a particular branch of medicine he will undertake a "residency" in that field. The latter usually requires an additional three years of training.

It was first developed through Dr. Rhenston that he was in his second year of "training" or "residency" at the time of Mrs. Alvaro's delivery and subsequent death. I then sought to show that the "attending" obstetrician was Dr. Herman Kurtz. In a hospital table of organization, the "residents" and "interns" are hospital *employees*, whereas the "attending" doctor is an experienced physician who voluntarily gives his services to the hospital and is in charge of the service involved.

In an effort to show that *at no time* while Mrs. Alvaro was in the Washington Hospital was the "attending" physician notified of her complications, the inquiry developed along the following lines:

Q. Doctor, whatever the name of the attending physician was, did you yourself at any time request that he be called in to consultation in Mrs. Alvaro's case?
A. I don't remember.
Q. Well, if you did, would it be noted on the chart?
A. Not necessarily. I wasn't in charge of the case.
Q. Who was in charge of the case—Dr. Colloway?
A. Yes.

Q. If the person in charge of the case were to request consultation with the attending, that should be noted on the chart, should it not?

A. That he requested or that he got the consultation?

Q. Well, both.

A. I imagine it would be on the chart.

Q. Beg pardon?

A. I imagine it would be on the chart, if he spoke to him.

Q. All right. In other words, if he spoke to whoever the "attending" is, and requested any consultation, according to the practice at Washington Hospital, that should be noted on the chart?

A. Yes.

Of course, the hospital record that had been offered in evidence showed that there was no "request for consultation," or *any* consultation with *any* doctor, let alone the attending physician.

It was now determined to show that following the delivery there was "hemorrhaging" and that while this represents a serious complication in any delivery, it is even more important when, as in this case, the patient is *anemic* to begin with.

Dr. Rhenston agreed with our original assumptions that a certain amount of bleeding *is* normal, but that when there are 500 cc's or more of blood following a delivery, this is called "postpartum hemorrhaging" and can be a serious matter. The doctor testified that Mrs. Alvaro had lost about 600 cc's of blood before she left the delivery room, and an additional 250 cc's some two hours later—making a total of about a *quart* of blood.

It was then shown that Mrs. Alvaro had been anemic on admission, as evidenced by a low hemoglobin count (the oxygen-carrying pigment of the blood), and that because of this she was in even more difficulty than might otherwise have been the case. Dr. Rhenston testified that a hemoglobin count of between ten and twelve grams was normal and that when Mrs. Alvaro's count was taken on admission, it was learned that hers was only 8.5, which represented anemia. He then admitted that for an anemic person such as Mrs. Alvaro, hemorrhaging in excess of 500 cc's of blood represented a *greater threat* than for one who had a normal count.

Having drawn a vivid picture for the jury of a hemorrhaging mother who was anemic, I was then ready to close in on the witness and show that the treatment she had received for this serious complication was *improper* and *inadequate*.

An important blood test, the "hematocrit" (showing the volume of red blood cells in relationship to the blood in the body), although *ordered*, was not done. The doctor testified that he had ordered a hemoglobin count and a hematocrit be done *immediately* and that this should be followed by the giving of the blood. Since it was a new word in the trial, I asked Dr. Rhenston to tell the Court what a hematocrit is:

A. Hematocrit is a packing of the blood to separate the cells from the serum.

Q. You felt at the time that you wanted a hemoglobin count done immediately and also a hematocrit count done immediately, or as you say stat, then to be followed by the transfusion; is that correct?

A. Yes.

Q. Because you felt, Doctor, that by doing in addition to the hemoglobin a hematocrit test—that's a simple test, the hematocrit?

A. They are both simple, yes.

Q. Simple tests. And when you do the hematocrit, it gives you a better picture of what this lady's blood situation is; isn't that true? Doesn't it help the situation?

A. It helps the situation, yes.

Q. Now, would you tell us, please what the hematocrit

that you ordered showed in Mrs. Alvaro?

A. *I don't find the hematocrit here.*

Q. As a matter of fact, Doctor, there was no hematocrit done on Mrs. Alvaro, despite the fact that you had
ordered it, was there?

A. I don't know. I don't find any in the chart. I'll have
to look through. I see the hemoglobin but not the hematocrit.

Q. If it was done, Doctor, it should be recorded on the
chart?

A. Yes, it could be in several places. If you will be
patient for a minute.

Q. You look, take your time, and you find for us any
place in that chart where the hematocrit that you ordered
not only to be done immediately but also to be done after
the transfusion had been given, you show us and read to
us one reading of one hematocrit that was done on Mrs.
Alvaro while she was in the hospital.

A. I don't find any hematocrit reading here. I only
find the hemoglobins.

Q. Beg pardon?

A. I only find the hemoglobin.

The absence of a hematocrit reading in the record made
a sharp crack in the defense. But now it was necessary to go
even further. I moved on to show that a dreadful error in
the treatment that had been ordered had occurred. Dr. Rhenston had written that the patient was to get a blood transfusion *immediately* (because blood lost can be replaced only by
more blood) and that then she was to receive an infusion of
glucose and water (routinely given as supportative therapy,
following most surgery). But what happened instead was that
the two instructions were followed in *reverse order:* Mrs. Alvaro got the infusion first, and then, not until at least two
hours later, did she get the blood transfusion.

Q. The order sheet shows, and you signed it and it's in your handwriting, that she was to be given 500 cc's of blood *immediately*—is that correct?

A. Yes.

Q. And after she had been given the blood, you wanted it to be followed by a thousand cc's of glucose and water; is that correct.

A. That's correct.

Q. Glucose and water is not a substitute for blood, is it, Doctor?

A. No.

Q. The only thing in the body that can replace blood that's lost is other blood—isn't that true?

A. That's correct.

Q. Now, isn't it a fact, Dr. Rhenston, that despite the fact that you in the order sheet when it was found that this lady was hemorrhaging and had lost at least five to six hundred cc's of blood and you ordered that she be given a blood transfusion of a pint of blood immediately and then be given an infusion, that whoever did it, did it in *reverse* and instead of giving her the blood immediately, gave her the glucose and water immediately, and it wasn't until about two hours later that she got the first blood transfusion? Isn't that a fact, Doctor?

A. No, I think that you are mistaken.

Q. All right. Get to the treatment chart. You say I'm mistaken.

A. Yes.

Q. You tell his Honor and the ladies and gentlemen of the jury what time did she get the infusion of glucose and water? Is it on the chart, Doctor?

A. I'm looking now.

Q. You look at it.

A. 8:40.

Q. 8:40 A.M., right?

A. That's right.

Q. She had delivered the second boy, you told us, about 8:20 something?

A. 8:25.

Q. So within ten or fifteen minutes she got the infusion of glucose—is that correct?

A. That's correct.

Q. And what time does the record show she got the first blood transfusion?

A. 10:30.

Q. So, Doctor, Mrs. Alvaro did not receive any blood at all until 10:30 in the morning—is that correct?

A. That's correct.

Q. I say it was about *two hours* after she had her initial postpartum hemorrhaging?

A. Correct.

The jurors were now sitting forward in their seats. It was apparent that they could scarcely believe what they had heard.

But now we moved to an even more important issue: that the blood Mrs. Alvaro had received was probably the *wrong type* and that it had not been *cross-matched* as required.

This was important to establish for several reasons. First, it would anticipate the defense that Mrs. Alvaro died because of a diseased liver condition. It was part of our claim that if she had been given mismatched blood the liver would have been affected. All blood that is given a patient should not only be of the same type but must also be cross-matched to make sure that, even though it was the same type of blood, the minor subdivisions of it were not in conflict. This is done by taking a sample of the patient's blood and mixing it with the donor's blood. Within about thirty minutes, it can be determined whether or not the blood is compatible. Actually, this cross-matching should be done *before* the delivery or the operation, so that the blood needed will be available immediately and thus not involve a delay when needed in an emergency.

Q. Doctor, let me ask you, was there any blood available to give Mrs. Alvaro when it was known on admission that she already was anemic and had a hemoglobin count of eight point something?

A. I believe so.

Q. Doctor, when a patient is cross-matched for blood, are there slips prepared showing that it was cross-matched?

A. Yes, they usually are.

Q. Would you show us, please, the slips showing that blood was cross-matched for Mrs. Alvaro?

A. I don't see it here. That's what I was looking for before. *I don't see the slips for the cross-matching.*

Q. If it was done, it should be attached to the chart—isn't that where it belongs, Doctor?

A. It belongs on the chart; that's correct.

Q. Now, I am asking you, is there anywhere on the chart, any slip showing that the blood that you gave her was cross-matched before they gave it to her?

A. *I don't find the slip here, no.*

It was now necessary to show that the treatment that had been effected was not helping the patient. In fact, Mrs. Alvaro's condition was deteriorating. Yet still no consultation had been requested. We established that the patient's hemoglobin count had actually dropped to 6.4; the doctor admitted that this was not a good sign. Then we pressed further, asking whether this drop was not, in fact, a sign of "impending danger." "Not necessarily," he answered.

Q. You say not necessarily, Doctor—

A. No.

Q. Isn't it a fact, Doctor, that one of the dangers of postpartum hemorrhage is that it may cause the death of the mother? Isn't that one of the great dangers?

A. Yes, it is.

Q. As a matter of fact, Doctor, postpartum hemorrhage is the major cause of maternal death in the United States?

A. Yes, I would say so.

Q. And so, Doctor, if you have a person who's bleeding and whose blood picture is not improving, that is a serious situation, Dr. Rhenston?

A. Not necessarily.

Q. If, of course, Doctor, the bleeding were to continue, that would be a grave sign—wouldn't it?

A. Yes, it would.

Q. That is a bad sign, isn't it?

A. It would depend upon how much bleeding.

Q. She's already bled, we have agreed, five to six hundred cc's; that's hemorrhage?

A. Yes.

Q. If a person's bleeding doesn't stop, that means its coming from somewhere?

A. Yes.

Q. Blood is contained in either an artery or a vein, that's where it belongs?

A. That's where it belongs, yes.

Q. If blood is leaking out, spilling out, that means that it's coming from either an artery or a vein; isn't that true, Doctor?

A. Or from—no.

Q. Or from an organ in which it's contained?

A. Exactly.

Q. Doctor, isn't it a fact that according to the hospital record, and we'll take your time, one o'clock in the afternoon, she hemorrhaged again?

A. She expressed some clots from—some clots, about 250 cc's of old clots expressed from the uterus, which contracts firmly. That's what it says here.

Q. Doctor, expressing clots means blood has collected and now an additional 250 to 300 cc's of blood clots were taken out of her womb?

A. That's correct.

Q. That is not a good sign, is it, Dr. Rhenston?

A. *No.*

Q. At that time, did you ask for a consultant to come in to see why this lady was continuing to bleed?

A. *I don't know.*

Q. Did you?

A. I, personally? I was not in a position to call. I was not supposed to call anybody.

Q. Do you know whether Dr. Colloway did?

A. *I don't remember.*

Q. We have agreed that if Dr. Colloway did it, a notation should be made on the chart that a consultation was requested? That's the practice, isn't it, Doctor?

A. It might have been put on the chart, yes. *It should be put on the chart.*

Q. You tell his Honor and the ladies and gentlemen of the jury if anywhere on this chart, there is a notation by anybody, that a consultation was requested in Mrs. Alvaro's case at any time.

A. With whom?

Q. Anybody—I am talking of the attending.

A. *No.*

Mrs. Alvaro's downhill course had continued, and it was shown that by the afternoon she had become *lethargic*—and *still* nothing was done for her.

Dr. Rhenston kept sparring as questions were asked about the patient's condition, and gave ground only when he was pressed hard. I read from the doctor's own notation that at about 2:30 in the afternoon, "Patient appeared comfortable and somewhat *lethargic*." When I asked him whether "lethargic" meant "stuporous or in a coma," he answered "In part." Pressed further, he said he did not think she was in a coma at that time, but he did admit that Mrs. Alvaro had become somewhat "stuporous."

What precisely did this mean?

I questioned Dr. Rhenston on this matter:

Q. It's true, isn't it Dr. Rhenston, that the blood as it circulates to the body goes to every tissue in the body, is that correct?

A. Not necessarily.

Q. Blood carries oxygen, doesn't it, Doctor?

A. Yes, it does.

Q. Doesn't the tissue, everything in the body, need oxygen, from the hair on your head to your littlest toe?

A. That's correct.

Q. Now, isn't it true, Doctor, that the brain, *the human brain requires more oxygen than any other organ in the body?*

A. That's correct.

Q. And when a person is suffering from a deficiency in blood because of loss of blood, one of the effects is what you doctors call *anoxia*—is that right, Doctor?

A. That's correct.

Q. Which means a lack of oxygen, correct, Doctor?

A. Correct.

Q. And when a person is suffering from a lack of oxygen, since the brain requires more oxygen than any other organ, one of its effects is to cause a condition of *stupor* in that individual? It may cause that?

A. Correct.

Q. All right. And that is what it caused in Mrs. Alvaro

at 2:30 in the afternoon, Doctor; isn't that true?

A. *I would say yes.*

As the examination of this important witness continued, it was shown that at 3:00 P.M., despite the fact that a second pint of blood had been administered, Mrs. Alvaro continued to get worse. Furthermore, it was developed that there were no slips showing that the blood she received had been cross-matched and shortly after receiving the blood the patient had developed a severe reaction:

Q. Now, Doctor, when she was given a second blood transfusion at about three o'clock, there should be a slip showing that the blood was checked and cross-matched?

A. Yes, there should.

Q. Is there such a slip?

A. I do not find it.

Q. Now, when a person following a blood transfusion has a reaction to it, is one of the signs of it, Doctor, the fact that she may—Doctor, will you just look at me a minute, please? That one of the things is that there may appear *jaundice*?

A. How long after?

Q. How long after what, Doctor?

A. Well, this depends. If you mean six weeks after, eight weeks after—

Q. How soon after?

A. No, you don't get jaundice in compatible reaction.

Q. Doctor, if a person is given blood which hasn't been cross-matched, may they *a few hours later* show evidence of some jaundice?

A. Yes.

Q. At any time during that day, did she appear to be jaundiced?

A. Do you have any specific notation in mind?

Q. Let me read to you, Doctor, from the nurses' notes. "At 3:30 P.M. color very pale. *Appears jaundiced.*" Is that right in the notes that the nurse wrote at 3:30?

A. That's correct.

Q. Which is now some five or six hours after the first blood transfusion and about a half hour after the second one was started?

A. That's correct.

It was then made clear to the jury that time was beginning to run out for Mrs. Alvaro, because at about 4:30 P.M. (about eight hours after delivery) her blood pressure, which on admission to the hospital was 110/60 (within normal range), had now started to drop so precariously that the patient went into shock. I asked Dr. Rhenston whether at any time the systolic, or upper, reading of her blood pressure had dropped to below 100. He began to refer to the notation made at 4:30 P.M., but I asked him to look at that for 11:00 A.M. first. This he did, and testified that it had then been 98/70:

Q. All right. That's not normal, is it, Doctor?

A. Yes, I think it is.

Q. How about when it goes below 90, that's not normal, is it Doctor?

A. It would depend. There are people who have normal blood pressure of 90.

Q. Doctor, what you are saying is this: If a person on admission had, as you say, a normal blood pressure of, say 90, that you would say is the normal, but if a person on admission to the hospital has a normal blood pressure of 110, 90 isn't normal for that person; is that so, Doctor?

A. 98 is.

Q. How about 88?

A. I would say 88 was low.

Q. All right. As a matter of fact, Doctor, when you

say low, 88 is an indication of shock or impending shock —isn't that true, Doctor?

A. Correct. It's one of the signs.

Q. Did Mrs. Alvaro's blood pressure ever drop to 88?

A. At 4:30 P.M. there is a notation that she was 88.

Q. So that at 4:30 in the afternoon, Mrs. Alvaro's blood pressure showed that she was already in shock or shock was impending; is that right, Doctor?

A. That's very difficult for me to answer.

Q. Didn't you just say before I asked you—

A. Yes. What you asked me is if it's one of the signs, yes. You put all the signs together and then you come up with a diagnosis of shock. . . . I would say that in answer to your question, yes, *that lowering of the blood pressure is an impending shock.*

Q. And Doctor, at that time did you request—or anybody connected with the hospital—consultation with the attending physician?

A. *I have no idea.*

Now we went even further, seeking to show that the neglect had continued. At 6:15 P.M. there was a notation—which I asked Dr. Rhenston to read to the court—that Mrs. Alvaro was still bleeding: "Bleeding P.V., per vagina, slight." It was now a full nine or ten hours after delivery, and the patient was still bleeding from the vagina. What further confirmed our claim that there had been, and still was, a general neglect of Mrs. Alvaro's condition, was that her *temperature* had not been taken at any other time than upon admission:

Q. Doctor, when a person is having a reaction to blood, is one of the things that might help in knowing that, is whether her temperature, whether there is a rise in temperature?

A. Yes, it may help.

Q. Now, could you tell us, please, in the fifteen hours that Mrs. Alvaro lived, fifteen, sixteen hours that Mrs. Alvaro lived, from the time of the delivery of the boys until the time she died, how many temperature readings were taken at Washington Hospital of Mrs. Alvaro? I want to know from 8:30 on?

A. I have one of 98.6.

Q. What time, Doctor? That was on admission, when she came in?

A. I assume that's on admission.

Q. Was there any other temperature reading taken of Mrs. Alvaro during the hours that I have just said? In other words, from the time of admission until the time she died, did anybody in Washington Hospital bother to take one temperature reading of Mrs. Alvaro to see if maybe she was running a temperature?

A. *I don't find any noted here.*

Our picture of gross neglect was now almost complete. There was still another area—namely, that the patient did not *void* once after delivery of the twins. This is an ominous sign, for it could indicate that the kidneys were not working properly. Dr. Rhenston, as in his previous testimony, was highly evasive—but he could not ignore the bald facts as they had occurred:

Q. Doctor, when a person has delivered of a child, voiding, that is, the elimination of urine, is an important thing that usually develops spontaneously.

A. Yes.

Q. And if, for example, a person is having an adverse reaction either to blood or particularly as to blood, is one of the things that's affected the kidneys?

A. Yes, it is.

Q. And may you have what you doctors call clinical

renal or clinical kidney shutdown, or in plain language, Doctor, where the kidneys aren't functioning right and you are just not eliminating? You are supposed to urinate and you are not; isn't that true?

A. When what? When the kidneys shut down, yes.

Q. Doctor, at any time following the delivery of these two little boys at 8:30 in the morning, until the time that Mrs. Alvaro died, did she once void? Will you look at the nurses' notes, Doctor, please?

A. One second, Counsel, please. She was catheterized at the time of the delivery.

Q. I am asking you *after* the delivery. "3:20 P.M. Has not voided as yet." Is that the note the nurse made?

A. That's what it says.

Q. That's not a good sign, is it, Doctor?

A. At 3:20 that she had not voided—if she had not voided, because you have to remember there were two shifts of nurses since then. I don't know.

Q. Doctor, if she had voided, isn't a nurse supposed to make a note of it in the chart?

A. I would imagine that she should, yes. And there is one here that she expressed the urine at the time of delivery. That she voided at delivery.

Q. I am asking you following the delivery, that's 8:30 in the morning. "At 3:20 hasn't voided as yet." That's a significant sign; isn't it, Doctor?

A. Yes, it might be.

Q. It's a bad sign; isn't it?

A. It would depend.

Q. Well, in a case where a woman is hemorrhaging, there is impending shock, she's not voiding, there is evidence of the fact that she has become jaundiced, she's continuing to hemorrhage, that's not a good picture, is it, Dr. Rhenston?

A. I can't agree with what you are saying. The picture

you are giving me is true, it's not a good one, but I can't say yes to all the things you are saying because I don't agree with some of them.

Q. Let me ask you this, Doctor: Take a look at 9:30 P.M. What does the nurse say about whether she voided?

A. "Has not voided yet."

Q. So then, Doctor, at 9:30 P.M., it's now thirteen hours and Mrs. Alvaro hasn't voided as yet. In fact, the nurse is making a note of that. That's not a good sign, is it, Doctor?

A. *If it be thirteen hours, it's not a good sign.*

Q. Do you question the accuracy of the notes made by the nurse, Dr. Rhenston?

A. You have a couple of shifts of nurses. I am not here to defend the nurses. I don't know. It would be a poor sign if she had not voided in that many hours, yes.

Q. Why is that, Doctor?

A. For what you had mentioned, about the renal shutdown. The possibility of renal shutdown.

THE COURT. The possibility of what?

THE WITNESS. Shutdown of the kidneys, that they are not working.

Q. At any time, Doctor, from 9:30 on, until the time she died, is there any note that she ever voided?

A. I can't find any, no.

Q. It's not in the notes, right?

A. There is no notation, that's correct.

There was still one final subject that had to be shown to the jury through the testimony of Dr. Rhenston: that for a period of about six hours before Mrs. Alvaro died *no doctor examined the patient,* who was, quite literally, in the throes of death. If this could indeed be demonstrated, wouldn't it be the proof positive that Mrs. Alvaro had died simply because *nobody cared?*

Q. From 6:15 until evening, until twelve midnight, which is a period of approximately six hours, did any other resident or any other doctor examine Mrs. Alvaro? In other words, from a quarter after six until almost before she died, which was a little after midnight, from 6:15 until midnight, did any resident examine Mrs. Alvaro? Yes or no?

A. Yes.

Q. What time?

A. Twelve midnight. The notation is at twelve midnight.

Q. I say, Doctor, from a quarter after six until twelve midnight, a period of almost six hours, no resident examined Mrs. Alvaro; is that a fact, Doctor?

A. No.

Q. Give me any other time that a resident examined her.

A. She was examined at—

Q. What time, Doctor?

A. Before midnight.

Q. What time?

A. I don't remember. She was examined several times. She was kept under observation and she was seen.

Q. Is there a notation in the chart?

A. No, there is no notation, except the one at midnight.

Q. We know about that.

A. But that was done before midnight. The notation was made at midnight but examination before.

Q. What time, Doctor?

A. Immediately before.

Q. A few minutes before midnight?

A. Right, the last one.

Q. Doctor, the chart shows that from a quarter after six, until a few minutes before midnight—

A. There are no notations, yes.

Q. Of any resident examining this lady; is that correct?

A. *There are no notations, correct.*

With Dr. Rhenston's admission that no doctor (no intern, no resident, and certainly no consultant) had taken the trouble to examine this dying mother for *six hours* prior to her death, the indignation of the jury was fairly manifest.

However, we still had to meet with the defense contention that Mrs. Alvaro had died of a preexisting liver condition. To do this we called Dr. Horace Webb, a medical expert who testified that, based on the many acts of gross neglect developed through Dr. Rhenston, there was indeed *bad medical practice* on the part of the defendant and that it had resulted in her death.

The defense called as its first witness, Dr. Silas Jones, the assistant hospital administrator.

Dr. Jones was called to show that he had searched for the records of cross matching of the blood and that though he could not find them, these records were usually destroyed after a few years. He further testified that since the cross matching in this case had occurred on a weekend, the house staff would have done the cross matching rather than the laboratory technician. The doctor told the court that the records of the blood that was given were kept in a ledger book.

We then cross-examined Dr. Jones as follows:

Q. Doctor, the slip with the blood itself, showing the type of blood that was given and the cross matching— where does that normally go? Doesn't it go with the chart?

A. Yes.

Q. When a bottle of blood is sent from the laboratory up to the patient, with the bottle of blood is there a slip?

A. Yes.

Q. Showing the patient's name, chart number, type of blood and that it has been cross-matched?

A. Yes.

Q. Now, what should be done—what was the accepted hospital procedure for Washington Hospital in 1959, what happens to that slip?

A. There have been several changes since then. In 1959, though, *I believe that the slip was pasted into the chart.*

Q. In other words, the chart is where the patient is; isn't that true, on the floor of the ward?

A. Yes.

Q. And the accepted practice was in 1959 that the slip should be attached, pasted into the chart?

A. Yes.

Q. Do you know where the slips are for Mrs. Alvaro in this case?

A. No, I haven't seen the chart, either, but I suppose they are not there if you ask me.

Then the witness's testimony about how the cross matching was done on a weekend at Washington Hospital began to assume ludicrous proportions:

Q. Doctor, do I understand you to say that in 1959, you say on a weekend, let's take a Saturday, that there was no technician, no qualified technician of the hospital working in the laboratory?

A. I didn't say that, but I can't tell you at this moment whether there was one or not.

Q. Doctor, if the patient has already gotten the blood that's wrong on Saturday, and it's not checked until Monday, that patient could already be dead, couldn't she, if it was wrong?

A. I couldn't answer that. That would depend on too many circumstances.

Q. Now, I'm asking you, Doctor, if on Saturday, for example, a patient needed blood in 1959 in Washington Hospital, the resident checked it and cross-matched it and it is given to the patient. What you are saying is, it wouldn't be until Sunday or Monday probably before the technician would double check to see if the resident did it right; is that what you are saying?

A. He would just check it.

Q. In what way—

A. *I don't see much sense to it, that's true, checking it again, but they did.*

Q. It doesn't make sense at all, does it, Doctor?

A. I didn't make that regulation; I'm just telling you what it was.

The last witness called by the defense was Dr. Clark Hosmer, City Pathologist.

Dr. Hosmer testified that he had performed the autopsy on Mrs. Alvaro and that he had found the cause of her death to be "acute fulminating massive liver necrosis." It was his opinion that this condition preexisted her admission to the hospital; that the condition of her liver was "irreversible"; and that nothing could have been done to save her. (It is interesting to note the similarity of this defense to that in the case reported elsewhere in this book, involving the intravenous pyelogram with subsequent convulsions and death.)

This testimony was a sharp challenge to our case. It was clear that if the plaintiff was to win, Dr. Hosmer's testimony had to be undermined. Otherwise, all the pains we had taken, in our examination of Dr. Rhenston, to establish the picture of *gross neglect* would have been in vain.

I decided to limit my cross-examination of Dr. Hosmer to one crucial area. Our exchange was short—but telling:

Q. Doctor, I just have a few questions to ask of you. I notice that you were very particular in answer to a question that was asked of you by Mr. Wunder, as to whether or not the hemorrhaging, this postpartum hemorrhaging that she had following the delivery of these twins, was the cause of her death, and I wrote down what you said, Doctor. See if I have written it down right. That it was not the *prime* cause of her death. Did you say that?

A. Yes, I did.

Q. Was it, Doctor, a *contributing* cause of her death?

A. It might have been. I can't answer that.

Q. In other words, Doctor, you are not saying to his Honor and the ladies and gentlemen of the jury that the bleeding, the hemorrhaging that Mrs. Alvaro endured following the delivery of these twins on July 18th, did not contribute to her death? You are not saying that at all, are you?

A. No.

Q. It might have been?

A. *It might have been. I don't know.*

This admission was exceptionally important to our case. The law in New York State and most jurisdictions is that a wrongdoer takes the plaintiff "as he finds him," so that a defendant who "contributes" to the death of plaintiff is as liable as if he was solely responsible for the death. The rationale for this rule is that a negligent defendant will not be permitted to argue that had the plaintiff been in better health when he injured him, the consequence would not have been as serious.

In cross-examination it is not always necessary to attack the witness: he can often be used as a sounding board for your position. This was the tack I took, utilizing Dr. Hosmer as my own witness. The long and important exchange that follows put before the jury a good number of revelations and admissions that appreciably strengthened our case:

Q. Now, of course, Doctor, as a pathologist, you are familiar, aren't you, with the various studies that have been made of mothers dying of hemorrhaging, what is called postpartum hemorrhaging?

A. Yes.

Q. You are familiar with that?

A. Yes.

Q. And it's true, is it not, Doctor, that postpartum hemorrhaging is the major cause, in the United States, if not throughout the world, of maternal death?

A. I suppose so.

Q. Are you familiar with the book *Clinical Obstetrics* by Drs. Tenney and Little?

A. Yes, I have heard about it. I don't refer to that book. I haven't referred to that book for any reason.

Q. Is it authoritative?

A. I think so.

Q. Doctor, do you 'agree with these statements by these authorities in a textbook—

MR. WUNDER. I object to that. We have not established that they are authorities.

THE COURT. Just continue.

Q. "The best treatment of hemorrhagic shock is its prevention."

MR. WUNDER. I object to that.

THE COURT. Objection sustained. The jury will disregard the question.

Q. Doctor, anoxia means lack of oxygen, and it's true, is it not, that the brain requires more oxygen than any other organ in the body?

A. It is true.

Q. And isn't it also true, Doctor, that brain cells, brain tissue, if damaged, the one thing about brain tissue different from any other tissue in the body is that it doesn't regenerate?

A. That is right.

Q. So that we understand what you are saying, Doctor, normally, for example, if a person were to injure his hand, nature would create new cells to take the place of the ones that were destroyed; is that true?

A. True.

Q. But brain tissue has a very special quality about it, namely, that if it is damaged or injured, it does not replace itself? That's true, is it not?

A. Yes.

Q. Now, anoxia means that the brain is not getting sufficient oxygen?

A. You should call it hypoxia. This is not anoxia. Anoxia is complete lack of oxygen. Nobody can live.

Q. Hypoxia?

A. Hypoxia.

Q. Of course, Doctor, when a person is bleeding and losing blood, it's blood that brings oxygen to all the tissues of the body, including the brain?

A. Yes.

Q. Now, Doctor, one of the parts of the brain is the pituitary—isn't it?

A. Yes.

Q. A very vital part of the human brain—is that true?

A. I wouldn't call it from the human brain. It's situated in the skull. It is a vital part of the endocrine glands.

Q. Is it part of the brain? Is it considered part of the brain?

A. If you want to call it generally, yes.

Q. All right. Doctor, do you agree with this statement, and I am talking now about anoxia and the brain, "that the longer the state of anoxia exists, the greater the danger of permanent and even fatal damage to the brain, pituitary, kidneys and other organs"? Do you agree with that statement?

A. That's a matter of opinion. I can't say that I agree or not.

Q. Well, Doctor, when you say it's a matter of opinion, are you saying that you agree or disagree or you can't say one way or the other?

A. I agree for part of it, that's all, because I'm not an expert.

Q. Now, Doctor, there is no question that you listed the second cause of death in Mrs. Alvaro's case as "infarcation of the pituitary, secondary to obstetrical delivery?"

A. It is not listed as the second cause of death. I did not say it is the second cause of death. It is the second finding on that. The only cause of death, according to that final diagnosis tabulated, is the first one.

Q. Did you say in this report, and I want to show you the final diagnosis, do you list on the final diagnosis six items? Do you, Doctor? Yes or no?

A. Yes.

Q. Do you stop after item 1, which is the "acute fulminating massive liver necrosis" and say that is the cause of death? Is that where you stop, or do you continue on and say, "second, infarcation of the pituitary, secondary to obstetrical delivery"? Don't you list them, one, two, three, four, five, six, in that order? Don't you?

A. I can't answer yes or no. I have to explain it.

Q. I am asking you whether you listed it in your report?

A. I want to explain it.

Q. Did you list it?

A. We list everything we find on an autopsy based upon the conditions that we find.

Q. In the order of importance that you list them?

A. Right.

Q. You list as first importance "the liver necrosis"?

A. Right.

Q. Second importance, "the infarcation of the pituitary, secondary to obstetrical delivery"—is that correct?

A. Yes.

Q. Now I am asking you if it isn't a fact, then, Doctor, that if a patient has undergone anoxia, lack of oxygen to the brain because of postpartum hemorrhage, whether or not it will not cause or may not cause damage to the pituitary gland?

A. Not that I know of.

Q. Was there an "infarction of the pituitary gland" in this case?

A. Yes.

Q. Doctor, do you agree with this statement, yes or no? "The longer the state of anoxia exists, the greater the danger of permanent and even fatal damage to the brain, *pituitary*, kidneys and other organs." Do you agree with that statement? Yes or no?

A. Yes.

This testimony by City Pathologist Dr. Hosmer had established two important facts for the plaintiff:

1. that the postpartum hemorrhaging *could have contributed* to her death;

2. that loss of blood causes lack of oxygen to the brain, which in turn can cause damage to "the brain, pituitary, kidneys and other organs." The autopsy confirmed that there had indeed been damage to each of these organs.

The defense then rested without calling any other witness.

The summation is often the difference between victory and defeat. At the conclusion of a case, most jurors are in a state of confusion. They have heard one witness say one thing, another witness something else—and they don't know whom to believe. It remains for the attorney to interpret all that has gone before, and he will use all the skill and experience at his command to tie the many loose ends into a lucid and clear picture that will direct the thinking of the jury in favor of his client.

In this case my opponent, Mr. Wunder, summed up first as required. He reiterated the position he took in his opening: namely, that the hospital is not obliged to provide the *best* of care but only *good* care; that simply because there was a bad result did not mean that anyone was at fault; that Mrs. Alvaro had not been a private patient at a hospital where she could expect minute-to-minute attention, but had been a ward patient in a city hospital and had, in fact, received *adequate* care.

Mr. Wunder further argued—with emphasis—that the cause of Mrs. Alvaro's death was not the hemorrhaging, but her preexisting diseased liver. She would, he said, have died of this prior condition, anyway.

When it was my turn to speak, I began with a simple unalterable fact: A woman had walked into a hospital to deliver a child, and within fifteen hours she was dead. Was this *despite* the fact that the hospital, through its employees, had treated Mrs. Alvaro in the accepted and proper manner—or had there been negligence, neglect, improper practice?

The only person who had said that everything was done properly was Dr. Rhenston, the second-year resident. Where was the attending physician in charge of the service? Where were *any* of the many doctors the city has on the staff of that hospital—or any of its other hospitals—to come forth and say, "The treatment was proper." By their absence, by their silence, I told the jury, it was clear that they were not called because they could not refute the plaintiff's claim.

Then I outlined the facts in the case: that postpartum hemorrhage is a serious complication, which, if not properly treated, may result in death; that proper orders were given for the patient to receive a blood transfusion immediately and then be followed by an infusion of glucose and water. But what had happened? Mrs. Alvaro was given the two treatments *backward*—and did not get the vital lifesaving blood until two hours later.

I reminded the jury that a blood study had been ordered but that someone forgot to do the hematocrit, without which they had not the vaguest idea of Mrs. Alvaro's blood picture. At 11:00 A.M. the patient had hemorrhaged again, an additional 250 cc's—an ominous sign; but no one had bothered to call a consultant. Yes, Mrs. Alvaro had received two blood transfusions—but they were not cross-matched, and perhaps were not even of the same type of blood.

Possibly the greatest image of sheer carelessness was the fact that the patient had not had her temperature taken at any time other than at admission: in the fifteen hours she spent in the hospital, during many of which she was literally dying, *no one bothered* to see if she was running a fever, and no doctor—during those last six hours—even took the trouble to examine her, despite the fact that the nurse's notes show that at 9:30 she was still bleeding. "Do you know why Louisa Alvaro died," I asked the jury. "Simply because *nobody cared*."

As for the defense that Mrs. Alvaro had a preexisting liver condition—where were the preexisting symptoms? The patient had received prenatal care at the hospital, and not one word was said that pointed to any prior liver disorder. If, as we suspected, she had received the wrong blood, that alone would explain the liver condition. But in any event, even if she did have a preexisting liver condition, the defendant's own expert does not deny that the hemorrhage *contributed* to her death.

And finally, having established our right to a verdict, I went on to the all-important matter of damages.

Though the law limits recovery in a death action to "pecuniary loss"—independent of the bereavement and sorrow to the next of kin—I asked the jury to consider the loss of actual services to Mrs. Alvaro's husband and her four children—the shopping, the cooking, the cleaning, the laundry work, not to speak of the parental guidance and moral training that only a mother can give her children:

> To us life is dear—one human life is priceless. We spend billions as part of our space program to see to it that there is a minimal loss of life to our astronauts.
>
> In a day when a Rembrandt painting can be sold for over two million dollars, who is there to say what the life of a mother is worth?
>
> The future of these children is in your hands. Their care and education will depend on your verdict.
>
> Who will be there to answer their question, 'Mama, what should I do?'—and who will be there to kiss away their tears?
>
> This is their day in court. Let your verdict be such that months or years from now, as you reflect on your decision in this case, let it be such that even then you will be able to view it with a sense of pride because it was a fair, just verdict.

The judge then charged the jury as to the law, and sent them out to deliberate.

In short order they returned a verdict for the plaintiff for $75,000. But the judge thought the amount too high, and granted a motion by the defendant to set the verdict aside unless the plaintiff agreed to accept the sum of $35,000.

When we refused this sum, the judge set the verdict of the jury aside and ordered a new trial.

Later, an appeal was taken by us to the Appellate Division. We asked for reinstatement of the jury verdict, or, as an alternative, that the case be sent back, to try damages only and not the liability of the city (which had already been established).

The appellate court granted our alternative request, and

when the case came up for trial as to damages only, the Honorable Harry Frank recommended that the case be settled for $60,000.

The city agreed to pay that sum, and we accepted it.

The settlement was satisfactory, and would be of much practical help to Mr. Alvaro and his four children—two of whom would never know their mother, who had died because *nobody cared*.

VII

THE MORTAL SIN

*A urological case—a kidney operation results
in injury to the ureter*

A leading urologist recently wrote an article entitled "Ureteral Injuries" that appeared in the official publication of the American Medical Association. Its opening paragraph read:

> Injury to the ureters during operation constitutes a serious surgical complication. The *venial* sin is injury to the ureter, but the *mortal* sin is failure of recognition.

The ureter is a tubular organ that connects the kidneys to the bladder; there are two ureters, one for each kidney. In size they are about the diameter of an ordinary straw, and twelve to fourteen inches in length. Urine, which is formed in the kidneys, is carried by the ureters to the bladder, where it is stored until it is ready to be eliminated from the body.

I was sitting at my desk some time ago when an obviously agitated lawyer phoned me about a new case. After introducing himself, he told me that his client was the plaintiff in a malpractice case that was to come up for trial shortly.

Though the case was over eight years old, they had still found no medical expert who would testify that the defendants were in fact guilty of malpractice. I started to say, "Sorry, there's nothing I can do for you," but the lawyer pleaded with me to read the file before I said "No."

In brief, he explained that one of the plaintiff's kidneys had had to be removed because of improper medical treatment. Some time later the one remaining kidney had developed tuberculosis—and now the plaintiff was in a bad way. Reluctantly, I agreed to read the file, and told him to send it to my office.

I scarcely realized what I had let myself in for. The file was voluminous. After spending hours pouring over the hospital records, pleadings, examinations-before-trial, and so forth, I felt that there was indeed malpractice. But could we prove it?

The practice in our office is to submit all doubtful cases to a conference discussion. A few days later, at a luncheon meeting held in the office library, I laid out the case before the office manager, Helen Danehy, and two of my partners, Henry Dillof and Peter DeBlasio. This was just before Tom Meagher had joined the firm.

The details of the case were as follows:

Vincent Mele was thirty-six years old, married and living with wife and one child. He had been employed since his discharge from the army after World War II by the Meyerhold Electric Company as a tester of electrical equipment, and now earned about $85 a week.

In March, 1956, Mr. Mele started to have a gnawing pain in the right side of his back, which came and went sporadically. After a few weeks, when the pain persisted, he went to see a local doctor, Dr. Richard Lawrence. The doctor examined him, proclaimed his ailment a "cold in the back," and gave him some penicillin shots. But a week later, the doctor decided it was "sciatica," and began heat treatments. This went on for several weeks, and then, when the patient still had no relief,

Dr. Lawrence had him admitted to the Bright Star Hospital.

At the hospital, the plaintiff met, for the first time, Dr. Leon Carnovsky, a urologist who had been called in as a consultant. Various tests, X rays, and urological studies were done, and it was determined that Vincent Mele's trouble was due to a condition known as a mild hydronephrosis of the right kidney. This is an enlargement of the kidney due to an aberrant blood vessel that has caused some urinary stagnation.

An operation was advised, and on April 27th, Dr. Carnovsky, assisted by Dr. Lawrence, performed the operation to eliminate the cause of the obstruction to the kidney—namely, the abnormally located blood vessels. The operation was routine and uncomplicated, except that at its completion it was noticed that there were burns on the *left* side of the patient's back. But this was only a minor complication. The real trouble developed after Mr. Mele was discharged from the Bright Star Hospital.

A few days after he got home he noticed a "wetness," or water, coming out of the operative wound on the right side of his back. It had a strong smell of urine.

Mele called Dr. Lawrence to tell him about it, but, as he later testified, the doctor said: "It's nothing. Don't worry about it. It's just draining." This went on for several days, and each day he was told the same thing: "Don't worry about it." Then, four or five days later, the doctor finally came to see him. When Dr. Lawrence saw the condition, he advised Mele to see the consultant, Dr. Carnovsky, immediately. This the plaintiff did, and Dr. Carnovsky then had him readmitted to the Bright Star Hospital.

Now the doctors discovered that the plaintiff had a "fistula" of the right ureter—an *abnormal* opening in the *ureter* that was causing the leakage.

Mele was kept in the hospital for three days and then *sent home* to await admission to another hospital a week later. But the day after he returned home from Bright Star Hospital, he became so sick that he had to be rushed immediately to the Veterans Hospital, where an emergency operation was performed. Because of the extensive damage to the right kidney, it could not be saved—and had to be removed.

A person can live with one kidney, but if the remaining kidney should go bad it could prove fatal. Unfortunately for Mr. Mele, he developed tuberculosis in his remaining left kidney, so that it was nip and tuck as to whether or not he would survive.

An action in malpractice had been started against Dr. Richard Lawrence, Dr. Carnovsky (who had since died), and the Bright Star Hospital.

After giving this detailed outline to my associates, we discussed the matter. Everyone agreed that the burns to the patient's back presented no problem of proof—but the injuries were of a minor nature. The larger question was: What about the ureteral fistula that had resulted in the loss of the kidney? Could we prove *that* to be negligence? We were unanimous that a urologist should be consulted for an opinion. That would help us to decide whether or not to accept the case.

Then an extraordinary development took place. A few days after our meeting, I made an appointment to see Dr. Jacob Weltz, a urologist. As I started to outline the facts to the doctor, he suddenly interrupted me and said: "The facts sound very familiar. Excuse me while I check my records."

He returned in a few moments with some papers in his hand, and said: "Mr. Kramer, the attorneys for the doctors consulted me a few months ago for my opinion about this case. I have rendered a report to them, so that I cannot be your expert."

I said: "That's understandable, Doctor, but could I ask you just one question? Do you think they will call you as their witness?"

Without hesitating, Dr. Weltz replied, "Not on the basis of the report I submitted."

I thanked the doctor, and left his office feeling elated. I knew I was on the right track—though there was still the problem of securing an expert to testify.

Often the simplest approach eludes us. We get so entangled in a maze of detail that what is right in front of us is obscured. It finally occurred to me to see the doctors at the Veterans Hospital. As luck would have it, the surgeon who had operated on the plaintiff, Dr. Marvin Green, was no longer connected with the hospital but was practicing urology in the city.

I have a theory about medical experts, particularly in malpractice cases, that has proved its worth through my years of practice. The best hope of getting one—always a difficult matter—is to do the necessary medical research in advance and ferret out the authorities and data that fortify your claim. It is one thing to ask a doctor for his opinion as to whether or not there was careless or negligent practice, but it is quite another to be able to spell out in detail the acts of negligence, support it with literature, and then ask him if he is in accord. When you have done the latter, the expert is usually more receptive.

Dr. Green was amenable, and since he was convinced that Mr. Mele had indeed been treated improperly, he agreed to testify.

I notified the attorney that I would accept the case.

In 1964, the case was assigned to be tried before Jenkin R. Hockert, an acting Supreme Court Justice. Tony DeCicco was trial counsel for the doctors, and the attorney for the hospital was Tommy Rizzo, a newcomer in trying a medical malpractice case.

In my opening statement, I outlined the facts and pinpointed our charges of negligence against the doctors as follows:

1. that the operation itself was unnecessary, as there was a paucity of symptoms and findings;

2. that if you are going to operate there are certain pre-operative tests that are essential—and they were not done;

3. that the operation was ineptly performed in that the ureter was injured;

4. that the postoperative care was bad, because despite complaints of urinary leakage, precious days went by before anything was done for the plaintiff;

5. and finally, that after the second admission to Bright Star Hospital, when the defendants discovered that the leakage was due to a ureteral fistula, Mele should not have been sent home.

As to the hospital, we implicated them only concerning the burns on the plaintiff's back: we insisted that they and the doctors owed the plaintiff an explanation as to how this had occurred.

The attorneys for the defendants denied any charges of negligence, saying that the surgery was difficult and that complications might indeed result in such cases without carelessness. The doctors, they said, had done everything they should or could for their patient.

I called as a witness for the plaintiff, the defendant Dr. Richard Lawrence. There was certain proof that I felt I could get by calling him in my case, rather than waiting for him to be called in the defense. There was also the element of surprise if I called him out of turn.

After covering the preliminary data, concerning when he had first seen the plaintiff and how he had treated him for several weeks, we came to the point where he had Mele admitted to the hospital and called in Dr. Carnovsky as a consultant. Dr. Carnovsky had recommended the operation, and I wanted to show that the witness agreed with the opinion of the urologist. But Dr. Lawrence began to quibble with me on this point. Actually, what I was asking was of no great moment, but his attitude clearly indicated to the jurors what they could generally expect of the witness:

Q. When Dr. Carnovsky decided that an operation was to be done, did you agree with it? Did you concur in his recommendation?

A. This is not up to me.

Q. Well, Doctor, Mr. Mele was your patient, wasn't he?

A. He is my patient.

Q. When Dr. Carnovsky recommended that an operation be done, did you agree with him, to his suggestion or recommendation that an operation be performed on your patient?

A. I don't have to agree. I mean, he is the surgeon in charge. He decides what has to be done, and this is it. I have nothing to say.

Q. Well, let me ask you: Were you present in the operating room?

A. Yes.

Q. Did you assist in the operation?

A. Yes.

Q. So, I take it, then, that you had no objection to the operation being performed?

A. I had no objection; that's true.

I then proceeded to question him about the burn that was found on the left side of the plaintiff's back—although the operation was on his right side. Again, the doctor tried hard to get away from responsibility to his own patient:

Q. When did you learn for the first time that his back had been burned?

A. I was told by the nurse.

Q. About what time, Doctor?

A. It was the same day, after the operation, the afternoon.

Q. What did you do?

A. I did nothing.

Q. What do you mean, you did nothing. I don't understand.

A. Dr. Carnovsky had the aftercare. That includes everything.

Q. You mean that you had no longer anything to do with the patient?

A. Nothing to do any more.

Q. Well, he was still your patient, wasn't he, Dr. Lawrence?

A. Yes.

He was then asked specifically about the burns:

Q. Doctor, what caused the burn on this man's back?

A. I don't know.

Q. Is there an antiseptic chemical used in the operation, in preparing the patient?

A. Yes.

Q. Do you know what antiseptic was used in preparing Mr. Mele for surgery?

A. I don't recall.

Q. Do you know what position the patient was in at that time?

A. During the operation?

Q. Yes.

A. Yes, he was lying on his left side.

Q. Who applied the antiseptic?

A. Dr. Carnovsky.

Q. Do you know what area he applied it to?

A. To the right kidney region.

Q. Was any of it applied to the left side?

A. No.

Q. Do you know whether any of it spilled down?

A. I don't recollect.

We now approached the very important subject of the urinary leakage, claiming that after the patient left the Bright
Star Hospital, urine had seeped from his wound for several
days and that, despite repeated phone calls by Mr. Mele, Dr.
Lawrence had ignored the complaints. When Dr. Lawrence
finally showed up and saw that it was urine, he immediately
advised the patient to see Dr. Carnovsky.

> Q. Now, how long did he remain at home? Or, we
> now know that he was at home from that date—what was
> that date, Doctor?
> A. May the 9th to the 20th.
> Q. Eleven days?
> A. Yes.
> Q. During that eleven-day period of time, did you
> see him?
> A. Yes.
> Q. How many times?
> A. Three times.
> Q. Do you have any record of those dates?
> A. *No.*
> Q. Have you checked any diary or records to indicate
> when you saw him at home?
> A. I mean, he lived in my neighborhood, and I thought
> I'd have to see him in his home. I didn't let him come to
> the office. I have no records, no.

It was the doctor's testimony that the leakage had occurred
the *very day* he saw the patient, or at most the night before.
But, as you will recall, the plaintiff's version was that the condition had existed for *many days* before the doctor showed
up. Concerning this crucial point, the following exchange
took place:

> Q. In other words, what you are saying, then, is that
> it is your recollection now that the urinary leakage must

have occurred the very same day that he called you to
come to the house?

A. Maybe the night before.

Q. Not more than that?

A. No more than that.

Q. It wouldn't have been for several days before that?

A. No, certainly not. I would have noticed it.

Q. You would have noticed it.

A. Surely.

Q. Well, now, Doctor, I want you to look at the
chart: "Several days after discharge, on May 14, 1956, the
incision opened and there was a large amount of urinary
discharge. This *continued* and the patient is readmitted
for investigation.

Now, Doctor, according to the entry on the chart
when Mr. Mele was admitted on the 20th, the history
given is that several days after he was discharged the first
time, which was May 9, namely five days later or six days
before he was admitted to the hospital is when the urinary discharge started, not the day before. Is that what it
says, Doctor? Look at it please.

A. Well—

Q. Just listen to me, please, Doctor. Does this refresh
your recollection that the urinary discharge started six
days, almost a week, before he was admitted to the hospital for the second time? Does it, Doctor?

A. Regardless of what the record shows here, as soon
as I saw the discharge, I notified Dr. Carnovsky and made
arrangements that he should see him again. So we don't
know—I notified him of what happened. How long before, I couldn't tell you.

The history on the second admission to the Bright Star Hospital confirmed the truth of the plaintiff's contention that he
was leaking urine for *almost a week* before he was readmitted

to the hospital. It was no less than gross neglect to permit this condition to continue so long, for unless corrected the toxic effects of the urine could destroy the kidney itself—which, in fact, it eventually did!

Concerning the second admission to the hospital, Dr. Lawrence again denied that he had any responsibility to his patient:

Q. Doctor, he was admitted to the hospital the second time on the 20th; is that correct?

A. Yes.

Q. Did you see him while he was there?

A. I saw him, yes.

Q. In other words, you saw him; he was still your patient—

A. I didn't treat him.

THE COURT. You what?

THE WITNESS. I didn't treat the patient in the hospital.

THE COURT. You didn't see him?

THE WITNESS. I saw him, yes, but I didn't treat him.

THE COURT. He didn't ask you that. He asked if you saw him.

THE WITNESS. Yes.

Q. He was still your patient, wasn't he?

A. He was Dr. Carnovsky's patient.

Q. Are you saying to his Honor and the gentlemen of the jury that he was not your patient any longer?

A. As a surgical case, no.

Every now and then the opposition hands you an unexpected gift on a silver platter. We had made the claim that the defendants should *not* have discharged the patient after the second admission—when it was found that he had a fistula causing urinary leakage. You can't sweep a patient under a rug, like dirt, in the hope that he will be forgotten. You have to treat the complication. Suddenly the doctor volunteered the information that the plaintiff had left the hospital "against the doctor's advice":

Q. How was he getting along the second time?
A. It's a matter of record.
Q. What is your recollection?
A. Dr. Carnovsky cystoscoped him again.
Q. Yes?
A. But he was only able to pass the catheter into the right kidney—he was unable to do it.
A. Yes?
A. There was an obstruction.
Q. Go ahead.
A. So he advised the patient to wait a few days, he may have it done again—to repeat it.
Q. Go ahead.
A. And, in the meantime, the patient walked out of the hospital.
Q. The patient walked out of the hospital?
A. Yes.
Q. Against the advice of the—
A. *Against our advice;* against my advice, at least.
Q. And you say he wasn't sent home to wait a week?
A. I think Dr. Carnovsky advised the patient that he wanted to wait a week before he did anything else.
Q. I am asking you if he wasn't sent home—sent home. Isn't that a fact?
A. *No.*
Q. Now, Doctor, in order for a patient to leave a hospital, unless he just walks out by himself, he has to be *signed out* by a physician?
A. A patient has to be signed out by the doctor for discharge.
Q. And wasn't he signed out by Dr. Carnovsky and sent home to wait a week? [Hands the witness the hospital record.]

A. *Yes.*

Q. Is there any note by Dr. Carnovsky that he left against the advice of the physicians?

A. No.

The doctor had just gone too far out on a limb, and he had given me an unexpected chance to cut him down.

Next I called Dr. Marvin Green, who would serve as our medical expert. Dr. Green was the surgeon who tried to repair the damage done by the defendants and who had, unfortunately, been required to remove the plaintiff's right kidney. Removal of a kidney is a major procedure, and is done only when there is no other recourse.

Dr. Green was very critical of the care and treatment the plaintiff had received at the hands of the defendants. He reinforced our charges by testifying favorably to a number of our contentions.

First, he stated that the operation performed by Dr. Carnovsky and Dr. Lawrence had been unnecessary:

Q. Now, Doctor, in your opinion with reasonable medical certainty, on the basis of the findings that I have read to you before, was this operation indicated?

A. I can't answer you in one sentence.

Q. I don't mean one sentence.

A. The man only had a very short history of pain— only went back several weeks. The X rays did not show any severe damage to the kidney. There is no severe hydronephrosis. There are various elements in the work-up which were lacking, so at that stage I, for one, would not operate on the patient.

Q. As a matter of fact, in your opinion, at that stage, was it good practice to operate?

A. No.

Second, Dr. Green went on to explain that certain vital tests that should have been done were omitted; the *urea nitrogen test*, which tests the blood, was one of these. "It's an indication of how well the kidney is functioning," he explained, "by ascertaining how much wastes are retained in the body. The kidney ordinarily excretes the wastes from the blood—it's a filter —and this is a test to ascertain just how efficiently it's operating and eliminating those wastes."

In addition, the defendants should have done a *urine culture*, "to determine whether there was infection in the urine," and a *delayed function test*, "to ascertain how much residual dye or how much dye was retained in the kidney."

Third, the operation itself was ineptly performed because it resulted in a ureteral fistula.

Fourth, Dr. Green was critical of the postoperative care. When the patient was home, complaining of urinary leakage *for four or five days*, not to have examined him was "very poor practice."

And fifth, when the patient was readmitted to the Bright Star Hospital and it was found that he had this fistula, he should not have been sent home, instead, "He should have had immediate surgery . . . to repair the fistula."

Dr. Green was an impressive witness. Not only was he on firm ground, but, what was even more important, he was the actual surgeon who had to repair the damage done by the defendants and was thus in a position to see precisely what their wrong practice had been and what its results were.

When the plaintiff, Vincent Mele, took the witness stand, he told his story simply and effectively. What had started out as a slight pain in his back had now destroyed his life. To make matters even worse, he and his wife had separated and he was now living alone. Although he was back at work, life for him had become a dismal routine. He was always tired, and had to save up the little energy he had in order to do a day's work.

I rested the plaintiff's case, feeling that we had proved our charges convincingly. I had no way of forseeing that the defendants would come up with a claim that I had not anticipated.

Tony DeCicco, attorney for the doctors, called as his expert Dr. Wilhelm Bortner, a diplomate in urology and Director of Urology at one of the leading hospitals in New York City.

After stating his qualifications, he mentioned the fact that my expert, Dr. Marvin Green, had been a student of his and that the preliminary tests Dr. Green had mentioned as *essential* are optional but not mandatory.

Dr. Bortner then had this to say about the operation and resultant fistula:

> Q. In the course of your twenty-two years as a urologist, have you had cases where surgery has been done and there has been a fistula developed?
> A. Yes, I create a fistula most of the time on purpose.

I couldn't believe my ears. The defense apparently was going to be that there is nothing wrong in a fistula developing, because, as the doctor had just said, he often created one deliberately.

During the untold hours I had spent in the medical library and among my own extensive collection of medical books preparing for this case, studying and researching every angle, I had come across nothing that resembled this defense. Furthermore, I had tried to anticipate every possible defense the opposition might come up with, and yet I had not foreseen this claim. Frankly, I was stunned.

Rather than question Dr. Bortner directly on this issue, I decided first to question him peripherally. This was the odd exchange that took place:

> Q. Doctor, when were you first consulted by the attorneys for the doctors in this case?

A. When was I consulted? The exact date, I am not sure. I believe it was last Friday, was it?—or—the date, I don't know.

Q. And, Doctor, did you render a written report of your opinion?

A. No, I didn't have an opinion.

Q. Well, when did you render an opinion?

A. I didn't render an opinion. You are telling me to answer something I wasn't asked to do.

Q. Well, were you asked for your opinion at that time?

A. Opinion of what, sir?

Q. What were you consulted about?

A. I was consulted to see if I would appear as an expert.

Anxious to show that the defendants had been shopping around for an expert before they latched onto Dr. Bortner, I asked: "Now, were you told at that time that the attorneys for the doctors had previously—only a couple of months ago —in fact, in June of this year—consulted another urologist by the name of Dr. Jacob Weltz?"

There was an objection to the question, and it was sustained "as to form." So I then asked:

Q. Did you see any written report which was furnished by this other doctor to the attorneys for the defendant? Were you shown such a report, Doctor?

A. I was merely consulted to ask if I would testify.

THE COURT. Just answer the question: Were you shown a report?

THE WITNESS. No.

I was now ready to question the witness about the fistulas he *created* "most of the time *on purpose*." I remembered from my reading of the medical literature on this subject that there

were times when it would be appropriate to cause an opening
in the ureter for drainage purposes—but that would be when
you were operating on a diseased or injured *ureter* and wanted
to divert the stream of urine. It had no bearing whatever on
this operation, and I wanted to show that the doctor was con-
fusing the issue.

> Q. Now, Doctor, I think we ought to get one thing
> straight, and that's this business where you said that there
> are times when you create a fistula on purpose.
> A. That's correct.
> Q. Under what circumstances is that, Doctor?
> A. Under the circumstances such as this case.
> Q. Is that a situation where you are dealing with some
> problem involving the ureter?
> A. Of course, that's when you do it, when you are
> involved with the ureter. That's the only time you do it.
> Q. In other words, is that where you have a diseased
> ureter?
> A. When you have an obstruction of the ureter, yes.

The doctor was now pinned down to a statement that it
is done where you have an *obstructed* ureter. The thing he
overlooked is that in *this case* there was no such obstruction
to begin with.

After many questions, and with the hospital report in my
hand to back me up, I finally got the doctor to agree:

> Q. In other words, Doctor, it says here that both
> ureters present *normal* appearance? Does it say that,
> Doctor?
> A. Yes.

Now I went on to the matter of the preliminary tests. Since
nothing came easy with this witness, it took persistent ques-

tioning to get him to make the following admissions concerning a test that was not done but should have been performed by the defendants:

> Q. Now, Doctor, in so far as the urea nitrogen is concerned, isn't it important before doing surgery involving the urinary tract to determine what the urea nitrogen is in the blood?
> A. It's as important as any other test, yes.
> Q. In fact, isn't it a well-recognized standard test done routinely in hospitals in New York City in 1956?
> A. Well, it's a standard routine test, yes.
> Q. And, in so far as this retention test is concerned, one of the things that is important to know, Doctor, is whether or not the kidney is emptying the urine on time or whether or not the urine is collecting and being delayed—isn't that one of the problems we are dealing with, particularly when we talk about stagnation in a kidney?
> A. That's right; that is important.

It seemed to me that the witness would probably not agree with the findings in the hospital record, to the effect that the *degree* of the plaintiff's original difficulty was "mild." In an effort to see precisely how the witness would react to this conclusion, I then asked:

> Q. Do you agree, Doctor, that whatever degree of trouble this man had in his right kidney, that it was *mild?* Do you agree with that, Doctor?
> A. No.
> Q. —insofar as the right kidney is concerned, that it was *slightly* dilated? Is that the way it's referred to, as visualized on the intravenous pyelogram?
> A. That's right.
> Q. And was the conclusion: "Mild stagnation in the

right kidney?" Is that what they used—the language right
in the hospital record?

A. Well—

Q. Is that what they said, Doctor?

A. They are saying more than that—that's taking it
out of text.

Q. Well, let me read it to you.

A. Read the whole thing.

Q. I am reading the conclusion: "*Mild* stagnation in
the right kidney, evidently due to an aberrant vessel."
Is that what it says?

A. That's exactly what it says.

Q. And if it says "mild," do you question the finding
and conclusion that it was mild at that time?

A. Yes.

Q. You disagree with it?

A. I *disagree* with Dr. Weisberg.

Dr. Weisberg was identified as the man who read the report, and, in answer to a question from the court, Dr. Bortner
said that this doctor was an "X-ray man, not a urologist."

THE COURT. Did you see the X ray?

THE WITNESS. *No.*

THE COURT. Go ahead.

Q. So, Doctor, is your opinion, then, based on the fact
that you disagree with Dr. Weisberg?

A. No, my opinion is based on my experience.

Q. Let's turn to the next page, where we now have
the retrograde pyelogram.

A. Yes.

Q. And it talks about the degree of hydronephrosis,
does it, Doctor?

A. That's right.

Q. And we have agreed, Doctor, there are three degrees of it, mild, moderate, and severe?

A. Well, that's what you said. I agree with that, yes.

Q. Now, is the degree of hydronephrosis that is reported in the retrograde pyelogram *mild* hydronephrosis? Is that what it says there?

A. By the same reporter.

Q. Do you disagree with him?

A. Yes.

Q. And you never saw the X rays?

A. That's right.

As I was questioning Dr. Bortner, my mind was still mulling over his testimony that he purposely causes fistulas and that this was what Dr. Carnovsky had done in this case. It was a matter of much significance, and I was very concerned about it because the jury would have no way of telling whether my expert, Dr. Green, or Dr. Bortner was telling the truth. However, I had the burden of proof upon me, and it was incumbent upon me to carry conviction.

Then, suddenly, a thought struck me: If Dr. Carnovsky had *intended* to cause a fistula it should be in the operative report. But I knew it was not there. At last I had found the witness's Achilles' heel.

My final questions probed directly at this issue:

Q. Did he cut the ureter in this case?

A. No, not according to his report.

Q. In other words, he at no time intended to cause a fistula of that ureter, did he, Doctor?

A. *If I read the report, no.*

The defendants then rested their case without calling any other witnesses.

At this point I decided on a bold move. Anticipating that

the defendants would not call Dr. Weltz, the man they had
first sought as an expert, I had subpoenaed him and called him
in rebuttal as my witness.

There was strenuous objection by Mr. DeCicco to the effect that I had no right to call Dr. Weltz. He was *their* expert
and, therefore, their "work product"—and thus could not be
used by me.

The judge overruled the objection.

Dr. Weltz testified to having been consulted by the attorneys for the doctor and of having informed them in writing
that:

> The need for surgery of the right kidney by Dr. Carnov-
> sky is questionable and subject to *medical criticism*. The
> existence of a mild hydronephrosis due to so-called aber-
> rant artery does not necessarily call for immediate sur-
> gery directly following cystoscopy, particularly when
> there was such a paucity of symptoms. It can be readily
> assumed that if there was such an aberrant vessel present,
> it was probably of a congenital origin, i.e., present at
> birth, and therefore it had produced very little obstruc-
> tion to the kidney urinary outflow in the thirty-odd years
> of the patient's life. The surgery was therefore *not* neces-
> sary.
>
> Similarly, the operative procedure by Dr. Carnovsky
> was *probably inept* and did cause an upper ureteral stric-
> ture and urinary fistula which made the latter nephrec-
> tomy mandatory; however, in Dr. Carnovsky's defense,
> no surgeon will guarantee a successful result in any oper-
> ation.

At the completion of Dr. Weltz's testimony, all sides rested.

The summations of all the attorneys were reiterations of the
original opinions of each. The defendants claimed: "We did
nothing wrong; it was difficult surgery and anything can
happen."

I, on the other hand, stressed the many points of criticism made by Dr. Green and the expert the defendants had elected not to call, Dr. Weltz. I reminded the jury that a lawsuit is not a game of wits, where one side tries to outsmart the other, and asked whether they would approve the practice of a defendant shopping around until he found an expert who would support their contention. I told them: "It was by pure chance that I stumbled on Dr. Weltz. What an injustice might have been done this plaintiff if I hadn't met him and brought him here to have you hear from his lips what he told the defendants. You will probably never sit in another case where the merits of the plaintiff's claim were so clearly proven."

Indeed, I was very confident that we would prevail, especially with the fortifying testimony that had been given by Dr. Weltz.

In short order the jury rendered a unanimous verdict for the plaintiff against the two doctors for $100,000, and against the hospital and the doctors for $6,000 for the burns.

But Vincent Mele's victory was short-lived.

The defendants appealed the verdict to the Appellate Division—one of their main arguments for reversal being that I had no right to call Dr. Weltz as my witness. I claimed otherwise, arguing that a party has the right to call *any* witness; that witnesses do not belong to one side or the other; and that since a defendant can call a doctor that treated a plaintiff, so I could call any doctor the defendants had consulted.

The Appellate Court thought otherwise. It agreed with the defendant's contention that it was improper for me to have called Dr. Weltz, and verdicts for the plaintiff were set aside and a new trial ordered.

I was very unhappy with this turn of events—especially since it was my act of calling Dr. Weltz that was responsible for the reversal; also, at the new trial I would not have the benefit of this doctor's helpful testimony.

Fortunately, the case ended happily. It came on for the second trial before Judge James Crisona who in short order, and to everyone's satisfaction, was able to arrange for the case to be settled for $75,000.

Vincent Mele had been the victim of gross negligence. It was only by the slimmest margin that the "venial sin" of injuring the ureter during an operation, and the "mortal sin" of not recognizing it, had not been fatal to him.

VIII

THE CASE OF THE
MISSING VITAL SIGNS

*A surgical case—removal of the thyroid
gland leads to brain damage*

Following any surgery in which
a general anesthetic has been given, as the patient is coming
out of the anesthesia the *vital signs* must be checked frequently; that is, the blood pressure, pulse, and respiration must
be taken and *recorded*, for they may be the clue to any impending complications. The case I am about to relate, involving a common operation known as a thyroidectomy, might
well be called—as I so named it in my summation to the jury
—"The Case of the Missing Vital Signs."

The thyroid is a small gland about two and a half inches
wide, situated in the front part of the neck, just across the
trachea, or windpipe; its function is to regulate body growth,
development, and metabolic activity by means of the iodine-
containing hormone that it produces. The most common thyroid complication occurs when it becomes overactive or enlarged—a condition commonly called a goiter. When this
happens, the body metabolism becomes too rapid, thus causing

155

the organs to function too quickly and thus eventually exhausting them. The patient becomes tense, nervous, and weak; sometimes he experiences a bulging of the eyes. The disease may be found in all age groups, but it is most prevalent in young adults, particularly women.

Surgery for the removal of the enlarged thyroid is safe and simple; it rarely results in complications. But there are always exceptions, especially if care is not exercised in the performance of the operation or in the postoperative period. To the patient, the cost of such neglect can be very dear. It was so in the case of Margaret Borgmann. Some instances of medical malpractice only *speak*—hers *shrieks*.

As a young girl of twenty-one, Margaret had come by herself to America from Germany. She stayed with an uncle, married a year later, and the following year became the proud mother of a little boy. Shortly after the birth of her son, she noticed that she was becoming very nervous and tense. She saw a local doctor, and was given some pills. When the condition still did not improve, she took a druggist's suggestion to see a surgeon, Dr. George Wilson. This she did, and after an examination he advised her that she had an enlarged thyroid that should be operated on.

Soon afterward, on May 2, 1958, Dr. Wilson performed a thyroidectomy at the Hillary Hospital in which he removed most of the enlarged goiter. The operation itself was routine, and no unusual complications were encountered. Since the hospital had no recovery room, the patient was transferred from the operating room directly back to her own room under the care of a nurse.

But a few hours after the operation, Mrs. Borgmann began to bleed profusely from the operative wound. She was brought back to the operating room, examined, and it was found that one of the ligatures tying off an artery had cut through the artery and was causing the bleeding. The artery was retied, and after she was given two pints of blood the patient was returned again to her room.

For the next few days Mrs. Borgmann did poorly. In fact, the day following the operation the nurse's notes showed that she was restless, convulsive, and had jerking movements of the arms and legs; she had also become incontinent of urine. There had still been no blood count or study ordered by the doctor to measure accurately how much blood she had lost during the hemorrhaging.

Then, five days after the operation, Mrs. Borgmann suddenly became partially blind and paralyzed. She had suffered a cerebral thrombosis—clotting of blood in the brain.

Mrs. Borgmann was later transferred to a second hospital, where she remained for three months. After this she returned to Germany, still suffering from impairment of vision and partial paralysis of an arm and a leg.

A lawsuit was initiated against the Hillary Hospital and Dr. Wilson, and eventually came to trial before Judge Harold J. Crawford. The hospital was defended by Frank Healy and the doctor by Harold Shapero. Shapero is associated with Martin, Clearwater and Bell, general counsel to the Medical Society of New York State: he has probably defended as many medical malpractice cases as anyone in the city.

In my opening to the jury I set forth my charges of negligence as follows:

First, Dr. George Wilson, the operating surgeon, had failed to perform proper hemostasis—that is, to tie off the left superior artery properly. In fact, he had tied it too tightly, because a few hours later it cut through the artery and caused the hemorrhaging.

Second, immediately after the operation there was evidence that Mrs. Borgmann was bleeding from the operative wound; Dr. Wilson should have investigated the situation at once, and not, as he did, waited until three hours later when there was profuse hemorrhage.

Third, the postoperative care was inadequate in that no proper studies were made of her blood picture, as a result of which there was an anoxia, with loss of oxygen to the brain and, five days later, the tragic cerebral thrombosis. I reminded the jury that six years after the operation, Mrs. Borgmann was still partially blind and partially paralyzed.

Concerning the hospital, I made one simple and unequivocal charge of negligence:

When Mrs. Borgmann left the operating room, helpless, she was placed in the care of a nurse, a hospital employee whose express job it was to check the vital signs and report to the doctor any unusual reaction of the patient: those signs had not been properly checked, and as a result profuse bleeding developed three hours after the operation.

The defense attorneys both denied the charges, each asserting that hemorrhaging following any operation such as this can occur even with the best of surgery and the best of care. Everything had been done for the patient, they asserted, that should or could be done: this was just one of those unfortunate situations that can happen—with no one at fault. Outstanding medical men in the field of thyroid operations would be produced to prove the justification of the position of the defense.

One of the greatest problems facing a patient who sues a doctor or hospital for malpractice is not only the laborious process of finding an expert witness who will say that the defendant indeed committed malpractice, but also, assuming such an expert has been found, the almost impossible task of matching the array of medical authority that a defending doctor can muster. In fact, in selecting a jury I will often alert them to this very difficulty of being unable to equal the defendant's experts, either in number or stature, by telling them how much easier it is for a doctor to get an expert to support him than it is for a patient. I ask prospective jury members whether they would be influenced by the *number* of witnesses called by the defense or by the *quality* of the testimony. This sometimes has a neutralizing effect.

In this case, as in any complicated case, the order of proof was important. Should you call your plaintiff first or last?

Whom should you put on the witness stand? Would it be helpful to call the defendants, or perhaps some of their employees?

Here, of course, calling Mrs. Margaret Borgmann herself as the first witness was a natural. She was now thirty years old—and, because of her obvious physical difficulties, a truly pathetic sight. In addition, she and her husband had been divorced some time after the catastrophe she had suffered, and she was now left alone, and incapacitated, to fend for herself and take care of her seven-year-old son. She was now living in Germany, and had returned to the United States just for the trial.

Mrs. Borgmann made a superb witness. She vividly portrayed her excellent health before the operation, and then outlined in some detail the difficulties she had suffered for so long, and continued to suffer: the partial vision and painful paralysis.

As my next witness I had subpoenaed Dr. Warren Maxwell, who had given the patient the anesthesia at the time the thyroidectomy was performed. Hours later he found her hemorrhaging and opened the wound, evacuated some blood, and then when the surgeon, Dr. Wilson, arrived, took her back to the operating room. Dr. Maxwell was not a friendly witness, but I wanted to bring out that when he got to her room at two o'clock, some three hours after she left the operating room, no one had alerted him to her difficulties.

Q. Doctor, the first time you saw Mrs. Borgmann after she had left the operating room was at about two o'clock?
A. That's correct.
Q. Now, did somebody call you to come to the room?
A. Not to my knowledge.
Q. Well, how did you happen—I mean, was it just coincidence that you happened to be in the room at the time?

A. No, I had finished my work in the operating room and I was making postoperative rounds.

Q. You walked into the room?

A. That's right.

He also testified how he found that she was cyanotic—that is, her body had turned blue. I wanted to show that because of the bleeding that had developed the patient was suffering from loss of oxygen.

Q. And when you noticed this cyanotic condition, what did that indicate to you?

A. Lack of oxygen. The patient was not getting any oxygen.

Q. And then what did you do?

A. I determined what the cause was and then I evacuated the blood which had accumulated in the wound.

Q. And what was the cause, in your opinion, Doctor?

A. The blood that had accumulated in the thyroid wound.

Q. And what effect was the accumulation of this blood having on her, Doctor?

A. Well, what it does, it obstructs breathing by compressing the windpipe or trachea.

It was now important to establish the necessity for the nurse to check and *to record* the vital signs, and to show that in the case of Mrs. Borgmann this had not, in fact, been done adequately. Coming from a witness closely connected with the defendant hospital, this information had greater impact:

Q. Doctor, what are the vital signs of a patient?

A. Well, you check the blood pressure, pulse, coloration.

Q. Respiration. These are the basic three vital signs?

A. That's right.

Q. And postoperative, when a patient has just come

out of an operation, is the checking of the vital signs an important part of postoperative care?

A. Yes.

Q. Doctor, how frequently should the vital signs be checked when a person has just come out of an operation?

A. At least every half hour.

Q. Is the accepted proper practice not only to take these vital signs, check them every half hour, but to *record* them on a record?

A. Yes.

Q. Doctor, do you see any notation in the record either in the nurse's notes or anywhere else in this chart of the taking and the recording of her vital signs, her blood pressure, her respiration or her pulse or coloration from the time she arrived in that room at 10:50 until the time you got there at about two o'clock and found this condition?

A. No, I don't see anything there.

Actually, two of the vital signs had been recorded by the nurse during that three-hour period: there was a blood pressure reading of 100/70, and a statement that the patient has a "rapid pulse." This, of course, was far short of the requirement to check and record *all* the vital signs at least every half hour.

I then called my experts, one a surgeon and the other a neurologist; they testified effectively as to the malpractice of the defendants as well as to the patient's present condition. In essence, the charges of negligence were as I had outlined them in my opening statement to the jury. But I knew then, as in almost every case such as this, that if a plaintiff is to achieve victory it must come from some fundamental weakness in the defendant's case.

A most interesting development occurred when the hospital was put to its proof. We had been hitting hard at the fact that the vital signs must not only be checked by the nurse but also *recorded*—and that there were no such records in the chart other than the two entries referred to earlier.

The head floor nurse, Mrs. Betty Walsh, took the stand and testified that she had looked in on the patient when she returned from the operating room. Although the nurse who was actually in charge of the patient was a Miss Alice Bragen, the witness herself had checked the vital signs at least four or five times. Mr. Healy, the hospital's attorney, questioned her as follows:

Q. Tell me, when you were in there, was any record of any sort being kept on anything so far as what tests were being taken and what the results were of the patient that morning by Miss Bragen?

A. Well, on the side of her bed there was a little chart for blood pressure, pulse and respirations which was checked.

Q. Is this a chart or a piece of paper?

A. It was a piece of paper.

Q. Will you describe it?

A. Well, it was a piece of scrap paper which we had columned off and we call it a chart.

Q. Were there entries on it by Miss Bragen when you went in?

A. Yes, there were.

Mrs. Walsh had nothing else to say about the paper. It was obvious from this that the defense was going to be that the nurses had not only checked the vital signs but actually recorded them as well.

Fortunately, there is always cross-examination to check on the veracity of the witness. A good starting point is the witness's memory. I consider "When is the first time anyone ever asked you about it?" an excellent question with which to begin. Usually it will have been at the trial, many years after the actual event, and you wonder how they recalled such a detail, especially if no written statement had been given.

> Q. When is the first time anybody asked you what you knew about the events of May 2, 1958? When, before taking the witness stand, did anybody ask you for the first time what you remembered about it?
>
> A. Saturday, this past Saturday.
>
> Q. The first time?
>
> A. Yes.
>
> Q. Had you ever given—just answer this yes or no—just any signed statement? Just answer it yes or no?
>
> A. No.
>
> Q. So that this Saturday was the first time anybody ever asked you any questions about the events in May of 1958, is that correct?
>
> A. That's right.

It was now important to determine more about that crucial "piece of paper" Mrs. Walsh had mentioned. Although the questions asked may seem trivial, they sought to establish how indifferently Hillary Hospital treated the all-important vital signs, as well as the dubious quality of Mrs. Walsh's memory:

> Q. How big was the piece of paper?
>
> A. A piece of, a half a piece of that yellow paper there.
>
> Q. Could you give us the size of it, about?
>
> A. No, I couldn't.
>
> Q. What was its size as related to the page of a chart?
>
> A. 4×8, I would say.
>
> Q. 4×8. In other words, was it about half?
>
> A. Half of that chart.
>
> Q. Half of this chart. Do you remember what the color of the paper was?

A. Offhand, no.

Q. Did it have lines on it?

A. No, it was a plain piece of paper.

Q. What was the color of the paper?

A. I don't remember.

Q. You don't remember the color?

A. White.

Q. You think it was white, or are you guessing?

A. *I am guessing right now.*

Q. And this record of the vital signs, doesn't that become part of the hospital record?

A. No, it doesn't.

Q. What do you do with it?

A. We just keep it at the bedside until everything is normal and then we *throw it away*.

Q. When was this thrown away?

A. After the patient's blood pressure and everything were normal.

Q. What time, I want to know.

A. It was after I went off duty.

Q. Do you know at what time it was that everything became normal here?

A. No, I do not.

Q. Is that the practice in Hillary Hospital, that the vital signs are kept on a piece of paper and then thrown away?

A. Yes. They are at the bedside until the patient's blood pressure and everything stabilizes, and then we throw it away.

Q. You don't attach it to the hospital record?

A. No, we do not.

Q. You do not? So that I take it, then, that there are no entries—that that's the place that entries are kept of blood pressure and pulse?

A. That's right.

The witness did not realize that actually there had been those two recordings of the vital signs on the nurse's chart. It must have seemed odd to the jury that some signs would be written on the chart while others were only put on a piece of paper. Clearly, they should all have been on one or the other.

Notice how Mrs. Walsh began to weaken somewhat when the following exchange took place:

> Q. Have you ever seen it since?
>
> A. It was thrown away, I *think*.
>
> Q. You *think*?
>
> A. By the evening nurse or the night nurse.
>
> Q. You just said you *think*. Is it that you are not sure?
>
> A. Well, I know it is not in the chart.
>
> Q. How do you know that?
>
> A. Because I put the chart together when the patient was discharged.
>
> Q. And did you see that that record wasn't there?
>
> A. Yes, I did.

The next witness for the hospital was Miss Bragen, the nurse who had been assigned to take care of Mrs. Borgmann. Miss Bragen—who turned out to be a practical, not a registered, nurse—testified that she recorded the vital signs on "a piece of paper" but that she would also write into the chart any "abnormal signs"—after which the piece of paper would be discarded.

As I began to question her, it occurred to me that the reason there were so few entries on the chart of the vital signs *might* have been that she was taking care of other patients besides Mrs. Borgmann. My hunch paid off:

> Q. I want you to tell us what other assignments did you have?
>
> A. Other patients to take care of.

Q. I want to know how many other patients?

A. I can't recall.

Q. Well, just stop and think. Can you give us an idea as to how many other patients you had taken care of that morning from seven o'clock up until the time Mrs. Borgmann came down from the operating room at about 10:50 A.M.?

A. I can't recollect.

Q. Can you give us an idea how many?

A. It couldn't have been more than five because we don't get more than five patients. It could have been less; I can't recall.

I then proceeded to question Miss Bragen on the importance of checking the vital signs, particularly of an unconscious patient—and also of recording them so that any change would be observed and new treatment initiated promptly. I had to establish what was a tremendously important and obvious aspect of the case: the curious vagueness surrounding the "piece of paper" on which the vital signs presumably had been recorded:

Q. And that record of the vital signs as checked, that's an important record, isn't it?

A. Yes, sir.

Q. What did you record your checking of the vital signs on?

A. A piece of paper on a table near the bed.

Q. Well now, this piece of paper, Miss Bragen, was that something, a form you were given by the hospital?

A. No, sir.

Q. The hospital, of course, has regular forms, haven't they?

A. Yes, sir.

Q. And they certainly have regular paper.
A. Yes, sir.
Q. In fact, they have their name printed on nurses' notes, temperature charts, respiration records, and so on, haven't they got a regular form for all that?
A. Yes, sir.
Q. Now this piece of paper, where did you get it from?
A. From the desk.
Q. And what was the size of it?
A. Pad size.
Q. Do you remember whether it had any lines on it?
A. No, sir, I can't recollect.
Q. In other words, you don't recall and you can't tell us whether this had lines on it or whether it was a clear piece of paper?
A. No, sir.
Q. You don't remember?
A. No, sir.
Q. Nor the color of it?
A. No, sir.
Q. What happened to that piece of paper, do you know?
A. No, I don't.
Q. What did you do with it?
A. *I can't recollect.*

The *coup de grâce* on the subject of the missing vital signs came when Miss Bragen tried to explain away the two entries, in her own handwriting, of "rapid pulse" and a blood pressure reading of 100/70 as being both normal *and* abnormal. The explanation that had been offered had been, you will recall, that "abnormal" vital signs would be recorded on the chart, while normal signs were recorded on the piece of paper. I asked the witness whether she had found that the patient had a rapid pulse. "No, sir," she answered. Then I pressed harder:

Q. Here, I will show it to you so that there is no question about it. Is that the entry? I asked you about it and you said that's in your handwriting, blood pressure 100/70.

A. 100/70.

Q. Is that normal or abnormal?

A. That's *normal*.

Q. And what time did you make that entry on the chart?

A. Between eleven and two.

I hoped that by this time the jury was beginning to doubt the hospital's defense. The feeble effort to explain away the vital signs by claiming that they had been recorded on a separate piece of paper, which was then discarded, was beyond credulity.

The hospital then called as its last witness Dr. Barnet Wilcox, a well-known internist. Dr. Wilcox asserted that in his opinion there had been no malpractice and that, in addition, the cerebral thrombosis that occurred five days after the operation was unrelated to the previous complication of hemorrhaging.

Having cross-examined Dr. Wilcox many times in the past, I knew him to be an honest witness, one who would give ground if asked the right questions. But which questions would lead to victory, and which to Pandora's box?

It was important to establish at the outset that Dr. Wilcox was not a surgeon and that he had not, in fact, ever performed a thyroidectomy.

It is extremely valuable in the cross-examination of a medical "expert" to invoke respected medical authorities. But first the witness must *recognize* them. After inquiring about six different books, which the doctor found unfamiliar or did not accept, we finally came to Dr. James H. Means of Harvard Medical School. Although unfamiliar with Dr. Means's textbook on endocrinology, Dr. Wilcox did recognize the author as outstanding in his field. This was a good start, for now it would be possible to show that hemorrhaging following a thyroid operation is a *preventable* complication. I began by reading a statement from Dr. Means's book:

Q. "Three complications. The result of technical *mismanagement* are peculiar to operations on the thyroid gland. 1. *Hemorrhage*."—and then they list the other two. Vocal Chord paralysis and tetany which, of course, is not involved here.

Do you agree with that statement, doctor? Yes or no?

A. No.

Q. Let me go on and read to you, and I am going to ask you whether you agree with this statement: "The incidence of all three complications is directly proportional to the *carelessness* with which the operation is performed and the possibility of their occurrence pleads for meticulous care in the avoidance of undue haste."

Do you agree with that statement?

A. Yes.

Q. You agree with that?

A. Yes.

Q. In other words, Doctor, do you agree, then, that the incidence of the complication of postoperative hemorrhage is directly proportional to the carelessness with which the operation is performed? Do you agree with that statement?

A. Yes.

Q. So then, Dr. Wilcox, it is recognized, is it not, that if the procedure is done carelessly, postoperative hemorrhage is one of the complications that will occur following a thyroidectomy?

A. *Yes.*

Q. Do you agree with this statement on the next page:

"The best treatment of a hemorrhage in a thyroid wound is its *prevention*. There is no substitute for the careful securing of all blood vessels."

A. *Yes.*

This admission, that to some extent hemorrhage following this type of operation is a preventable complication, was valuable. It was next necessary to challenge Dr. Wilcox's opinion that there was no relationship between the cerebral thrombosis that occurred on May 7th and the hemorrhaging that occurred several hours after the operation:

Q. Doctor, was it your opinion as stated in your report that part of the difficulty that this lady was suffering from, from the period of May 2nd to May 7th, was the fact that there had been a marked blood loss?

A. No, I don't believe I said that.

Q. Well, let me ask you, Doctor, isn't it a fact that some of the difficulties that this woman suffered from on May 7th were due to the fact that there was a marked blood loss as evidenced by the fact that even after getting these blood transfusions on May 7th her hemoglobin count had dropped from 80 percent to 55 percent?

A. No.

Q. Dr. Wilcox, let me ask you: There is no question, is there, that this lady sustained a cerebral thrombosis on May the 7th, is there?

A. I would not be sure that she had a cerebral thrombosis.

Q. Now, Doctor, do you disagree with the diagnosis in the Hillary Hospital report that this lady suffered and sustained a cerebral thrombosis on May 7th and the diagnosis in the Aldrich Hospital to which she was removed, that it was a cerebral thrombosis of the basal artery—do you disagree with that?

A. *Yes.*

This was like manna from heaven. Here was the defendant's own expert, who had never treated the patient in the hospital and who had never examined her afterward, not only disagreeing with the diagnosis of the defendants themselves as recorded in the hospital record but also with the diagnosis of the second hospital Mrs. Borgmann entered.

I decided to complete my questioning of Dr. Wilcox by making him my own witness, since Mr. Healy had not gone into the problem of the vital signs in his direct examination.

> Q. Isn't there a standard practice that postoperative the vital signs of a patient be taken and recorded?
>
> A. Surely.
>
> Q. And isn't it true that these recordings, since they are of the vital signs, are very important as part of the hospital record?
>
> A. Yes.
>
> Q. And become part of the hospital record?
>
> A. Yes.
>
> Q. Have you heard of any instance where the vital signs do not—are discarded—in your experience?
>
> A. I don't know of any specific instance.

Mr. Healy completed his defense for the hospital shortly thereafter, with no new evidence forthcoming. It was then time for the doctor's defense to begin.

Harold Shapero called Dr. George Wilson himself as his first witness.

Dr. Wilson, who appeared quite professional, made a good witness. He described the operation in some detail, the hemorrhaging that occurred three hours later, the retying of the artery, and the complications that developed five days after the operation. He testified that all his actions had been in accordance with proper medical practice and that he was not to blame for the complications that had unfortunately transpired: they were unavoidable.

Once again, since the most effective cross-examination in medical malpractice cases is often the use of medical textbooks that contradict the witness, I was anxious to show that authoritative literature said hemorrhaging was an *avoidable* and not an unavoidable complication following a thyroidectomy. After Dr. Wilson recognized Lewis's *Practice of Surgery*, a twelve-volume work, as a standard text, I began my cross-examination:

Q. Now, Doctor, I am going to ask you whether you agree with this statement which is under the heading "Complications Following Operations upon the Thyroid Gland."

That's what we are dealing with here, Dr. Wilson?

A. Yes.

Q. "Immediate postoperative untoward results. 1. Hemorrhage."

Is that what we are dealing with here, Doctor?

A. Yes.

Q. "In the event bleeding should occur immediately following operation, this unfortunate and *avoidable* complication as a rule develops within six hours."

Do you agree with that statement, Doctor, contained in this book?

A. As a rule it develops within six hours.

Q. I am not asking you about the part about it developing within six hours. I am asking you where he says here that it is an *avoidable* complication. Do you agree with that statement? Yes or no?

A. No.

Q. Let me go on and ask you whether you agree with this: "The most common source of blood is from one of the thyroid arteries." That's true, isn't it, Doctor?

A. Yes.

Q. "The ligature"—that means the tying off?

A. Yes.

Q. "—either loosens as a result of improper tying or is split off by the pulsating vessel due to the same cause."

Do you agree with that statement, Doctor?

A. No, I don't agree with that.

Q. Let me ask you whether you agree with this statement, same page, same paragraph, talking about hemorrhage following a thyroidectomy:

"That an ounce of prevention is worth a pound of cure is indeed a pertinent truism here, for hemorrhage cannot occur following thyroidectomy *unless hemostasis has been imperfect.*"

Do you agree with that statement, Dr. Wilson?

A. I have got to agree with that one; sure I agree with that one.

I had the feeling that the doctor did not understand the last question. It was too good an admission, and I did not want to take advantage of the answer, because if he agreed that hemorrhage does *not* occur unless the tying off has been imperfect, it was a confession of guilt. I decided to give the doctor a chance to get off the hook:

Q. Hemostasis, so that we understand it, that means the tying off of blood vessels?

A. That's right.

Q. And there is no question, Doctor, that one of the things a surgeon should do when he performs an operation, any operation, is to make sure that he properly ties off blood vessels; that's true, isn't it?

A. That's right.

Q. And it is certainly true of arteries?

A. That's right.

Q. You have got to make sure you have tied them off properly, otherwise they are going to slip off or cut through; isn't that true?

A. That is true.

Q. So that do you agree, then, with this statement, that "hemorrhage cannot occur following thyroidectomy unless hemostasis has been *imperfect*."

Do you agree with that?

A. The *imperfect* part I do not agree with.

Q. I thought possibly you didn't understand the question. That's why I wanted to read that part to you again, where it said here that you cannot get and will not get hemorrhage following a thyroidectomy if you have tied off the arteries properly. That's what it said, right?

A. That's what the book said.

Q. You don't agree with it?

A. I don't agree with those parts.

During Mr. Shapero's direct examination of the defendant, Dr. Wilson had repeatedly asserted that the ligature had "slipped" off. Our claim implied otherwise, of course: we insisted that the reason for the postoperative hemorrhaging was that the left thyroid artery had been tied too tightly, with the result that it had *cut through* the artery, which then started to spurt blood. As I began my final questioning of Dr. Wilson, I reminded him that the phrase "slipped off" had been used constantly in Mr. Shapero's examination. He admitted that it had.

Q. Now if, of course, an artery has been tied off too tightly, then what may happen is it will *cut* through; isn't that one of the complications that may develop if the surgeon has tied the artery off too tightly?

A. That's a possibility.

Q. Well, Doctor, isn't what happened in this case the fact that not that it slipped off but that it probably cut through the artery; isn't that what happened here?

A. It is a possibility.

Q. Well, I am asking you—you know the difference between possibility and probability, Doctor?

A. Yes.

Q. Possibility is anything, right? In other words, if I said the moon is made out of green cheese, it is a possibility until we get a man up on the moon and decide what it is made up of. Maybe, I don't know; it is unlikely. But if somebody said it is a possibility, you couldn't disprove it, right?

A. Yes.

Q. On the other hand, when we speak of something as being probable, now we are talking of something within the realm of likelihood and more in the area of certainty, isn't that true?

A. Yes.

Q. Didn't you in the hospital record in your own handwriting, Doctor, when you did the religation, after the hemorrhage and you brought her back to the room, didn't you write here "religated" and then in parenthesis *"suture probably cut through"*?

A. I did.

Q. So the probabilities are, then, Doctor, instead of the word "slipped" that has been used right along in the direct examination by Mr. Shapero of you, that what you said in the hospital record is not the word "slipped" but that it "probably *cut* through," isn't that what you said?

A. In that record I did.

Q. Doctor, this is the record. Did you make this record the very day it happened?

A. I did.

Q. Was it your opinion at that time?

A. At that time.

Q. Have you changed your opinion?

A. *Yes.*

Though the doctor could claim that his original report was inaccurate, we felt that the last vestiges of his defense had in fact been torn aside. In his own handwriting he had written that the suture had "probably cut through." Did he have *any* cause, other than a desire to avoid guilt, to justify that judgment made at the time of the religation? It seemed scarcely possible.

But there were still more medical experts to be contended with.

The next defense witness was Dr. Steven McGill, a surgeon with superb qualifications. Though Dr. McGill readily testified that on a basis of his knowledge of the case there had been no malpractice, in cross-examination he had to admit that there are both avoidable and unavoidable complications that may develop in such thyroid operations. When asked whether tying off the artery too tightly, if indeed that could be proved, were good practice, Dr. McGill admitted that "No, it is not good."

I then decided to see if I could make some headway with the fact that immediately after the operation there was evidence, duly noted by the nurse, of a "rapid pulse" and also of "moderate bleeding"—which, three hours later, became profuse:

> Q. With reasonable medical certainty, Doctor, in a thyroidectomy may a rising pulse be an early warning sign of impending hemorrhage?
> A. I would say no to that in a thyroidectomy.
> Q. Well, is a rising pulse of significance?
> A. Not in a thyroidectomy; not in this particular one location.

I had struck out. Many lawyers say, "Ask in cross-examination only those questions that you are sure of the answer." That is too narrow a mold. You must have a certain maneuverability in your questioning. Where one thing fails, another may succeed, as witness what happened to the matter of "moderate bleeding." Here I seemed to have hit pay dirt.

Q. Generally, Doctor, is bleeding postoperative following a thyroidectomy of significance?

A. Yes.

Q. And assume there is a moderate amount of bleeding postoperative, is that of significance?

A. Yes.

Q. Why?

A. Because it is bleeding into a closed space, and a relatively small amount of blood can cause a compression of the windpipe and produce a sudden asphyxia.

Q. And, Doctor, if you had operated on a patient and were informed that postoperative there was a moderate amount of bleeding, would you investigate that situation?

A. Yes.

Q. Doctor, I want you to assume that in addition to a moderate amount of bleeding there was a rapid pulse. Under those circumstances, would it be good practice to investigate the situation?

A. Yes.

Q. And what would you do, Doctor?

A. Talk to the nurse, look at the dressing.

Q. You, yourself?

A. Look at the patient.

Q. You, as the surgeon?

A. Try to, yes.

Q. In other words, you would want to investigate to see whether it is of any consequence or not?

A. Yes.

This admission that a combination of bleeding and rapid pulse warranted further investigation was a helpful start. It now seemed appropriate to broach the all-important subject of the "missing" vital signs again:

Q. It is true, is it not, that if a patient is watched carefully and observed you may be able to pick up, be alerted to signs which may prevent, later on, complications?

A. Yes, in general that's true.

Q. That's the whole purpose of it, isn't it?

A. Yes.

Q. Now, Doctor, these vital signs, am I right in saying not only should they be taken, but recorded?

A. Yes.

Q. Is that standard practice?

A. Yes.

Q. And is the recording of these vital signs important?

A. Yes.

Q. And that record, the recording of it, in your experience, does that become part of the hospital chart?

A. Yes, it does.

Q. Have you, in your experience, ever heard of any practice in the hospitals you are connected with where the vital signs would be recorded on a piece of paper and then thrown away? Did you ever hear of that practice, Doctor?

A. Offhand I don't remember ever having it happen. Some funny things do happen.

Q. Have you, in your experience, Doctor, ever heard of any practice—I am not talking about some idiosyncrasy or some unusual situation—but have you ever heard of any practice in a hospital in the City of New York that you are familiar with, where the vital signs post-operative are recorded on a piece of paper which is then thrown away?

A. No, I haven't heard of that.

I concluded my cross-examination of the witness by referring to Lewis, to his statement in *Practice of Surgery:* "An ounce of prevention is worth a pound of cure is indeed a pertinent truism here, for hemorrhage *cannot occur* following thyroidectomy unless hemostasis has been imperfect." I asked Dr. McGill whether *he* agreed with that statement.

"Yes," he said.

> Q. In other words, unless, say, an artery wasn't tied off properly, you would get as a complication postoperative hemorrhage?
>
> A. *We always take the blame for things like that.*

The answer had been so perfect that I felt like saying to him, "Dr. McGill, we ought to pay part of your fee for testifying, because you have been more than helpful."

The final witness for the defense was Dr. Donald Harper, a well-known blood specialist. Under Mr. Shapero's direct examination, Dr. Harper testified that the blood picture had been properly managed by Dr. Wilson and that it had not been necessary that the patient be given any additional blood transfusions.

Despite Dr. Harper's impressive qualifications, the facts of the case seemed to indicate that there was at least a reasonable possibility he was wrong. After all, Mrs. Borgmann had been given one quart of blood three hours after the operation, *but no blood study had been made* to see if that was the right amount. She might indeed have needed more blood at that time. It was not until May 7th, when Mrs. Borgmann had the cerebral thrombosis, that a blood count was done, and it had shown a marked drop in the hemoglobin:

> Q. Doctor, if in this case a blood count had been taken within twenty-four hours after the postoperative hemorrhaging, the blood picture of this lady would be in the hands of the doctor—he would know what her blood loss was?
>
> A. If you mean he would know how much she lost the day before, yes, that's true.

Q. And they would also know, Doctor, wouldn't they, what the hemoglobin picture was?

A. That's how they would estimate it.

Q. Now, Doctor, there is no question, is there, that based on the blood count which was done on May 7th, that she had lost following this hemorrhaging on May 2nd more blood, considerably more blood than had been replaced?

A. Yes, I computed that she had lost probably two quarts where she got back one quart, based on the blood count.

Q. In other words, on some computation you have made?

A. Based on the hemoglobin taken later.

Q. This lady, Mrs. Borgmann, this patient had lost two quarts of blood?

A. Probably.

Q. Whatever the figure is, there is no question she had lost more blood than she had been given?

A. There is hardly any doubt that she had lost more blood than she was given.

Q. That she had lost actually on your computation *twice* as much blood as she had been given?

A. Probably.

Q. And there is no question, is there, Doctor, that taking a blood count is a very simple procedure, isn't it?

A. It is.

How simple—and yet how costly the failure to take the blood count had been for the patient!

With his last answer, I was able to wave the witness off the stand, for Dr. Harper had effectively confirmed what my own expert had said: Because the patient had got back an inadequate amount of blood, there was a loss of oxygen to the brain that resulted in the cerebral thrombosis a few days later.

When Dr. Harper stepped down, all sides rested. We adjourned to sum up the next day.

For me, the summation is the most fascinating part of the trial, and I look forward to it with great anticipation. Every now and then, after I have prepared it, the case will be settled just before the summation is to be delivered, leaving me with a letdown feeling, a feeling that something within me must now remain bottled up. Over the years, I have developed a regular pattern of preparing my summation long before the case has been concluded. Sometimes, after my opponents have completed their opening statements to the jury and the issues have been clearly delineated, I already know what my summation will be.

Careful preparation for the summation is imperative, and I invariably review all my notes of the trial, including the opening remarks of my opponents and a reevaluation of the exhibits that have been marked in evidence. Then I draw an outline of my proposed remarks.

The heart of the summation is, of course, the analysis of the issues in the case. Those issues on which we are on firm ground are a good place to start, and from there one can gradually work up to those that are more in dispute. Wherever feasible, actual quotes, even brief ones, from the testimony given by a witness at the trial make effective additions to a summation.

But no matter how thoroughly you prepare your remarks, you must still retain a certain amount of flexibility in your comments to the jury, depending on what your opponent has said to them in his concluding remarks. He might, for instance, have tendered a challenge: "I would like to have Mr. Kramer explain to you why he never produced as a witness the family doctor, who clearly should know more about the plaintiff's condition than anyone else." Should you answer this or not? Quick decisions are called for. A sound rule of thumb is, if you have an effective response to the question, give it; otherwise, you are probably better off if you just ignore it.

Harold Shapero, in behalf of Dr. Wilson, summed up first. He discussed the medical issues in a characteristically thorough and scholarly manner, and concluded that Dr. Wilson could only be recognized as blameless.

Frank Healy, in his summation in behalf of the hospital, noted at the outset that the hospital was *not* responsible for the acts of Dr. Wilson, but only for those of their own employees. He stressed that they had done nothing wrong, but had, in fact, actually saved Mrs. Borgmann's life.

When it was my turn, I spoke first about our charge of negligence against the hospital, pointing out that in the three-hour period following the operation there were only two vital signs recorded in the nurse's notes. Everyone, including the hospital, realized that *if* those were the only vital signs checked in that period of time, this would constitute improper care. So we were told of the signs being checked every fifteen minutes and recorded on a "piece of paper." "But what happened to the *piece of paper*?" I asked. "Nobody knows. And if I were to give a heading to the claim against the hospital, I would call it *The Case of the Missing Vital Signs.*"

I stressed the importance of this piece of paper, how vital signs meant "vital to the *life* of the patient"—but how vague and contradictory the head nurse's testimony had been. She had said that only "abnormal signs" were recorded on the chart, but then had asserted that the two entries were normal. "They can't have it both ways," I argued. If the readings were abnormal, why wasn't something done? If they were normal, why were they the only two—presumably of many —entries on the chart?

I concluded my remarks about the hospital by recalling Mr. Healy's comment that the hospital employees had actually "saved" Mrs. Borgmann's life. On the contrary, I argued, if the nurse had indeed done the job she should have done, and which she could not possibly have done properly while attending "up to five patients," Mrs. Borgmann would never have found herself in a situation where her life was threatened.

The heart of our claim against Dr. Wilson was that he had not tied off the artery properly, with the result that it cut through and caused hemorrhaging. I reiterated his testimony, quoting directly from the court records to show first that he had admitted that tying off an artery too tightly is bad practice, and then had denied that this was what he had done.

"Gentlemen," I said to the jury, "this really defies imagination. It is almost like Alice in Wonderland. Records are no longer records, and words no longer have meaning. Remember how I asked Dr. Wilson, 'Doctor, didn't you, the very day you took her back to the operating room, when you wrote your report, didn't you say, "Spurting left superior thyroid found. Religated"—and we *know* this means tied off, again—"suture probably *cut through*." ' Cut through. Those are not my words. And even if the suture had *slipped* off," I told the jury, "don't think for a moment he wins a prize, either. I don't care, in the final analysis, whether it slipped off or cut through, because it just shouldn't do either if you do it right."

I then dealt with the fact that authoritative medical literature, as highlighted in the testimony, established that postoperative hemorrhage following a thyroidectomy *was due to carelessness*. Even the medical "experts" produced by the defense had, albeit reluctantly, admitted this. When I asked Dr. McGill, the expert called by Mr. Shapero, "In other words, unless an artery wasn't tied off properly you would not get as a complication postoperative hemorrhage?"—what did he answer? "In a low voice," I told the jury, "and I don't know whether you heard it at the time but it is the answer to the whole case, Dr. McGill said, '*We always take the blame for things like that.*' "

The balance of my summation dealt with other points of negligence, such as the failure to recognize the postoperative signs of impending hemorrhaging and the failure to check Mrs. Borgmann's blood and replace it with the proper amount: it had been *sheer carelessness* to guess that she had lost only one quart of blood when she had actually lost twice that much. A simple blood test, *which was never done*, would have given them the answer.

The jury found in favor of Mrs. Borgmann, in the sum of $100,000—against both the doctor and the hospital. Although I was glad to have won the case, I was, frankly, disappointed with the amount awarded.

Wasn't the plaintiff entitled to a larger verdict? After all, Mrs. Borgmann was now partially blind and painfully paralyzed—and would be, for the rest of her life.

IX

WHO DID IT?

*An orthopedic case—an elbow operation
results in injury to the ulnar nerve*

Among the many problems that
confront a patient who wants to sue a doctor, getting *jurisdiction* of the alleged wrongdoer can be one of the most difficult. This issue will arise if the patient and the doctor, or
hospital, are from different states. For example, if a New York
resident is operated on in *another* state and is injured because
of alleged malpractice, he will have to hire a lawyer in the
doctor's state (assuming the doctor does not also practice in
New York State) and bring the action there. This can create
insurmountable obstacles, though a breakthrough sometimes
occurs.

Such is the story I am about to relate—a case further complicated by the often difficult question of which of several involved doctors was actually guilty of medical negligence.

Larry Enright, forty-seven years old, was a New York
resident whose business frequently took him to various states
in the East. At a conference in Washington, D.C., he met
Dr. Milton Winston, a local orthopedist with whom he had
occasion to speak for several minutes.

Little did Larry realize how that meeting would affect the future course of his life.

Dr. Winston, noticing that Larry could not straighten out his right arm, inquired about the difficulty. Larry told him that when he was about eight years old he had received a sharp blow to his right elbow and that at the age of fourteen he had started to lose motion in the elbow. His mother had taken him to see Dr. Meyer Lausch, a prominent orthopedist, but after about a year of treatment there was no discernible improvement.

When he was twenty-eight, Larry went to see another orthopedist, a Dr. Schwartz, who performed an operative repair on his elbow at the Flower and Fifth Avenue Hospitals. Actually, there were two operations performed, and following them there was marked improvement in motion. The result was that Larry, who now had *no pain*, could engage in such sports as bowling, golf, and ping-pong. But he could not fully straighten his right elbow and arm (extension), and could not fully turn the wrist (supination).

Dr. Winston asked Larry if he had any objections to being examined. He didn't, and the doctor, after looking at the elbow and taking X rays, told the patient that an operation on the elbow would both straighten out the arm and give full motion to the wrist. After discussing the problem with his wife in New York, Larry agreed to undergo the operation.

The day following Larry's admission to the Harding Hospital in Washington, D.C., Dr. Winston performed an operative procedure known as an "arthroplasty of the right elbow" (correction of the right elbow joint), during which he removed a piece of bone that had overgrown and was causing the restriction in the joint. Following the operation, the patient's right arm was placed in a plaster cast. He remained in the hospital for about ten days and then continued to be treated at the doctor's office, daily, for another ten days.

The patient claimed that immediately after the operation

performed by Dr. Winston, he noticed that two of the fingers of his right hand had become numb and that after a while the hand had taken on the appearance of a "claw." He said he complained to the doctor about the condition, but the doctor made light of it, saying it would clear up in time.

Larry Enright returned to New York about a month after the operation and immediately went to see a New York orthopedist, Dr. Harvey Fabricant, who diagnosed that the "claw" hand had occurred because the ulnar nerve had been severed. He had the patient admitted to the Andover Hospital within six weeks of the operation done by Dr. Winston, where a transplant (repair) of the ulnar nerve was performed. Unfortunately, the repair was unsuccessful. A year later, a second attempt at surgical correction of the condition was performed, but it too failed to remedy Larry's problem. The patient was thus left with a right hand and arm that were of little use to him.

Larry Enright consulted some lawyers in New York and was told that since Dr. Winston was not a resident of New York he could not be sued here. Then he went to see some lawyers in Washington, D.C. They frankly told him that they could not get an expert to testify against this well-known orthopedist, no matter what malpractice he might have committed.

Thus the problem of jurisdiction was compounded by the greatest obstacle that confronts an attorney in an action against a doctor: the "conspiracy of silence."

The problem is of exceptional importance, and it is worth interrupting the narration of Larry Enright's case briefly in order to explore it further. There are towns, cities, and even states in this country where it is virtually impossible to get one doctor to testify against another, however flagrant the malpractice. Though the medical profession has referred to the "conspiracy of silence" as a "false phrase" that has no basis in fact, a doctor's fear that if he testifies for a plaintiff

he may be ostracized or criticized by other doctors often leads
him to renege on what is virtually a public responsibility.

How well I remember *my* medical expert who, on the
stand, listened intently to a question as to whether a particular procedure was the basis of good practice and then, hesitating, answered, "Yes." I was shocked. He had just told me
privately that it was "bad practice," and had assured me that
he could give three good reasons why. A few days after the
trial he apologetically explained that as he started to testify
he noticed, seated in the courtroom, the Chief of Service of a
hospital with which he was connected; assuming that the
doctor was a defense witness, my "expert" had feared to an-
tagonize him.

The recent book *Intern* is said to be a true account of the
author's experience as an intern at a "first-rate" hospital. In
it, the author tells of a woman who had a routine varicose
vein ligation done at another hospital by a general practitioner
who accidently cut the femoral *artery* instead of the saphenous *vein*. The woman was brought in for a repair of the
error, but little could be done, and the chances were that the
leg would have to be amputated.

The author tells how he commented to his superior (the
Surgical Resident) that it was hard to understand how any
doctor could make such a mistake and that it seemed to him
"the gal should sue for every nickel she could get and that
every doctor in town should be with her right down the line."

The Resident shook his head, saying: "It could be you next
time, just as well, and then what? . . . You just can't nail the
man for making the mistake, and as for negligence, there isn't
a doctor alive that isn't negligent one way or another every
week of the year. So how can you crucify this guy just because he happened to get caught? *You go pointing fingers
and you may find yourself in a very slippery spot sometime
with a whole lot of fingers pointing at you.*"

The author then had some second thoughts, and makes this

observation: "I guess nobody is going to say anything much, just tell this woman that this was an *unfortunate complication* of her surgery and see what happens." Hippocrates must have taken a few spins!

Concerning this whole important issue of a "conspiracy of silence," Judge Carter of the Supreme Court of California, as far back as 1951, stated in an opinion:

> Regardless of the merits of the plaintiff's case, physicians who are members of medical societies flock to the defense of their fellow member charged with malpractice and the patient is relegated, for his expert testimony, to the occasional lone wolf or heroic soul, who, for the sake of truth and justice has the courage to run the risk of ostracism by his fellow practitioners and the cancellation of his public liability insurance policy.

More recently, a leading New York jurist, the Honorable J. Irwin Shapiro, in the case of *Charleton v. Montefiore Hospital*, quoted with approval the following:

> No matter how lacking in skill or how negligent the medical man might be, it [is] almost impossible to get other medical men to testify adversely to him in litigation based on his alleged negligence.

As for Larry Enright, he now had his back to the wall. He had been crippled by the carelessness of a doctor, but had no remedy. In addition, Dr. Winston had been continually billing him for $850, his charge for the operation and for postoperative care.

Larry refused to pay.

Matters stood like this for some time, but just before the Statute of Limitations (the time within which a patient may sue a doctor) ran out, a miracle occurred: Dr. Winston sued

Larry for the $850—in the Civil Court in New York County. That was just what was needed to get jurisdiction against Dr. Winston, and we immediately appeared for Larry, serving a general denial to the doctor's suit, and, in addition, a counterclaim against the doctor for malpractice. Though a plaintiff can sue only for up to $10,000 in the Civil Court of New York, there is no limitation as to the court's jurisdiction in a counterclaim.

The malpractice insurance company for Dr. Winston now appeared for him, and soon afterward the case came on for trial before Judge Bernard Nadel. Sherman Bernhardt, who is associated with Dom Cornella, was counsel for the doctor.

The proof in this case was quite different from most malpractice cases in that here the plaintiff was the doctor and the defendant was the patient. Consequently, the plaintiff doctor had to present his case first.

In his opening remarks, Sherman Bernhardt told the jury how he would show that Enright had had difficulty with his right arm for at least fifteen years before he came to Dr. Winston; that the operation performed by the doctor was in accordance with proper medical practice; and that following it there were no complaints made to the doctor. In fact, he would prove that Enright drove a standard-shift car from Washington back to New York. Furthermore, when the patient got home, a member of his family, observing the improvement, had referred to Dr. Winston as a "genius." The counterclaim for malpractice, he concluded, was an afterthought to avoid meeting a valid obligation: Dr. Winston's bill for $850.

In my opening statement to the jury, I explained that a counterclaim rather than a direct suit was being brought against the doctor because jurisdiction was not possible until the doctor had sued Enright in New York.

I pointed out that Enright's right arm gave him no pain before the operation, and had very little wrong with it; that it was Dr. Winston who had urged the operation by assuring Enright he could improve the condition of his arm; and that following the operation there were numbness and pain which the doctor ignored. I said we would prove that when the patient got to New York he immediately consulted Dr. Fabricant and gave him the history of what had happened; this doctor subsequently found that the ulnar nerve had been lacerated, and the arm now had to be operated on again. Good medical practice required that the ulnar nerve be *identified* and moved away from the operative field, so that it would not be injured during the course of surgery: that to injure the nerve is bad practice.

The first witness called by my opponent, Sherman Bernhardt, was Dr. Winston himself, who promptly testified to his many years of practice as a specialist in orthopedic surgery. He then told of meeting Enright and of examining him; the disease that caused the patient's trouble, he said, was probably *tuberculosis* of the bone. Finally, he went on to describe the operation he had performed on the elbow, telling the court how he had removed a piece of bone that was causing the restriction of motion.

What he had to say about the ulnar nerve was important: it was the crux of our claim. He said he did not find it in its regular groove, but saw some scar tissue about one-half inch away, indicating there had been a previous *transplant of the nerve;* he "assumed" the nerve was in that mass. Dr. Winston did not attempt to isolate the nerve because, he stated, it would only make matters worse; in any event, he did not cause any injury to the nerve during the course of his operative procedure—of this he was sure.

Dr. Winston, a man in his late sixties and quite distinguished in appearance, had made an excellent witness—at least on direct examination. When I had taken the doctor's examination-before-trial—a preliminary inquiry, under oath—as to his version of what happened, I had noticed that the doctor did not like to have his statements questioned. Armed with this knowledge, I planned my cross-examination to prick the veneer of the doctor's "superior" attitude quickly.

Cross-examination is the tool by which a witness's truthfulness can be tested. There is no better weapon available to the adversary system than to require a witness to answer any and all questions that are relevant to the inquiry—to test his mental capacity, veracity, and accuracy. The *art of cross-examination* comes down to the simple but all-important matter of preparation. There is no substitute for planning in advance of the trial what your line of attack will be. Even Perry Mason has to read his script before he gets to court!

I believe in hitting the witness early in cross-examination with something that will cause the jury to view his testimony critically—before they might have developed a favorable view of the witness. One of the most effective ways of questioning a witness is to confront him with something he himself has written. This was done as follows:

Q. Have you had occasion to testify in court as a witness on many occasions?

A. Numerous occasions.

Q. As a matter of fact, Doctor, you wrote an article that appeared in a medical periodical recently, in May of last year, known as *Medical Economics* and the title of this article was "Tips on Testifying: How to Get Through to the Jury." Is that the nature of an article that you wrote for *Medical Economics*?

A. Yes. This is an article.

Q. Is it, Doctor? Yes or no.

A. Yes, it is.

Q. In other words, Doctor, did I read correctly the title of this article "Tips on Testifying: How to Get Through to the Jury"—is that correct?

A. That's correct.

Q. And in this article, did you say, "As an orthopedic surgeon who has been called in as a medical witness more times than I care to remember, I know what it is like to have an opposing attorney zero in." Did you say that in the article?

A. The *editor* said that I did.

Q. Was it over your signature?

A. Yes, I agreed to it, but the editors phrased it; I didn't.

Q. You mean you didn't write it?

A. It was edited.

Q. You mean you didn't write this article?

A. I prepared the article, and the editor edited the article and changed it.

Q. Whatever the editors changed or reedited, in the final analysis, whatever was submitted for publication to the medical profession on "Tips on Testifying: How to Get Through to a Jury" was over your name—is that correct?

A. That's correct.

Q. And you had the final approval, didn't you, as to what the editor or anybody else was going to say in this article?

A. That's correct.

Q. And is this statement an accurate statement, that you have had occasion to testify in court more times than you care to remember; is that correct?

A. I think it is correct.

Though it had been purely by accident that I came across this article, it proved to be a good starting point. It quickly showed the jury that the witness was just as much at home in the *courtroom* as he was in a *hospital*. It also showed that he would be agile in trying to explain away anything that might embarrass him.

The next area that I explored was the matter of the doctor's *office records,* and why they were not in court. Bear in mind that after the patient's discharge from the hospital in Washington, he went to the doctor's office daily for about ten days, where he complained about the condition of his hand and showed it to the doctor. Dr. Winston denied this. Wouldn't the doctor's office records be the best evidence in this instance? Where were they?

I established that the *cards* the doctor had produced were merely ledger cards for billing purposes, and that his true office records—on which he would record whatever complaints a patient had had and whatever findings he had made —were not present. At first the doctor said that as far as he knew, he thought the cards that had been produced were the only records about this patient. A moment later he said, "I don't have the file with me, so that's all I remember." "You mean," I pressed, "it may be in your file in your office?" The doctor answered, "It is possible, yes."

Now notice how he starts to change his course:

Q. Well, now, Doctor, we know and you have testified and your ledger card shows that after he got out of the hospital, you saw him approximately a dozen times. Is that correct?

A. I think so.

Q. Well, have you got those records here?

A. No, I don't.

Q. Where are they, Doctor?

A. I guess they are in my file *if there are any.*

Q. You mean this is the only record you have brought here; is that correct, Doctor?

A. That's correct.

Q. Did you look for the other records?

A. I *suppose* I did, yes.

Q. Well, did you, Doctor?

A. Yes, I did.

Q. When?

A. Before I came.

Q. Well, you came here when, Doctor? A couple of days ago? You came here yesterday. When did you arrive in New York?

A. Sunday night.

Q. And did you look for your records on Sunday?

A. Yes, I did.

Q. So, you did look for them?

A. Yes, I did.

I then left the subject of the doctor's records to go on to other matters. A little later, however, when I decided to return to this theme, the following exchange took place:

Q. Now, Doctor, I asked you about this earlier. . . . I assume that your office records of these visits, these *ten or twelve visits* that he made to your office after he was discharged from the hospital—I assume those records would show (A) if he complained about anything to you, and (B) what, if anything, you found. Is that true, Doctor?

A. Sure.

Q. Have you got those records?

A. No. I *refreshed my memory* and I think I can answer your question.

Q. Well, Doctor, would it be too much trouble for you to produce those original records so that we can have them in court here?

A. I can try. I can get them, I think.

Q. When you say you refreshed your recollection from them, when did you do that, Doctor?

A. Before I left.

Q. In other words, on Sunday?

A. Yes.

Q. You looked at those records on Sunday?

A. Yes.

Q. And how many pages were they, Doctor?

A. One or two. One, maybe. I don't know. I don't remember now.

Q. Is there any reason, Doctor, why you didn't bring your original records of treatment you gave this man and his complaints to you, while he was under your care from the time he was discharged from the hospital on July 20th to August 2nd?

A. No. I don't think there is any reason.

Q. When will you have them for us, Doctor?

A. What was the question? When will I have them?

Q. Yes.

A. *Well, I think I can get them by tomorrow.*

It now appeared that the good doctor had seen his own vital office records as recently as a day or two before the trial and that *he was now prepared to produce them in court.* But when he was questioned about the testimony he had given at the pretrial examination, when he said he could find no other records than those marked in evidence, this extraordinary exchange occurred—and those records started to disappear again:

Q. "Q. Do you have any other record of any kind which indicates your findings or his complaints or the nature of your examination of him when he came to your office following his discharge from the hospital. A. No, I don't."

Were you asked those questions and under oath in 1963 did you give those answers?

A. Yes, I did.

Q. Were they true?

A. Yes.

Q. Well, didn't you just tell us before, that you've got in your office somewhere something you saw on Sunday, other records indicating the visits that he made to your office after he was discharged from the hospital. Didn't you say that?

A. I don't believe I have any other records pertaining to this particular point that you have raised.

Q. Did you just tell us a few minutes ago that you have records of his office visits to you, his complaints and your findings, that you refreshed your recollection on Sunday and that you were going to bring us those records tomorrow? Didn't you tell us that just before, Dr. Winston?

A. I said that I would bring anything I had pertaining to this case, *but I am not sure now what that is.*

The third point that I sought to make very clear was that the doctor was completely wrong in his diagnosis that the patient had *tuberculosis* of the elbow joint, a very serious condition:

Q. After examining him and taking the X rays, I understand you made a diagnosis that your patient was suffering from tuberculosis of the bones of his elbow. Is that your diagnosis?

A. I guess that's right.

Q. Now, Doctor, tuberculosis, of course, of a bone is a very serious condition?

A. It is.

Q. And as you said you can't really tell even by looking at an X ray or examining a patient clinically whether they have or haven't got tuberculosis; is that correct?

A. It is not accurate, no.

Q. There is, however, an accurate procedure for determining whether a patient has or hasn't got tuberculosis, and that is the pathologist's report?

A. That's correct.

Q. When bone or any kind of tissue is removed following an operation, it is the accepted procedure for that tissue to be sent to the laboratory, the pathologist for microscopic analysis; is that correct?

A. That's correct.

Q. And it is the trained pathologist with his scientific instruments who can determine what the particular disease of that tissue is: is that correct?

A. He does try. He tries to determine that.

Q. Now, I assume Doctor, that in this case, after you had performed your operation of July 10th, you sent bone tissue and whatever pieces you took out of his elbow to the pathologist?

A. I did.

Q. Now, Doctor, would you look at the pathologist's report, please, and tell us whether or not the pathologist says one word of finding any tuberculosis in this man?

A. *There is not.* I said that there is not.

Having set the stage by my preliminary attack on the witness, I was now ready to approach the heart of the case—the operation itself. It is important that we understand something about the anatomy of the elbow joint. If you hold your right arm out, palm up, the portion of the elbow closest to your body is called the medial side. This is the side where the ulnar nerve is located. The outside of your arm is called the lateral side, and the back of the elbow is the posterior side.

Dr. Winston had made his opening incision on the posterior-lateral side (the outside and back) of the elbow. There is some question as to whether that was the proper approach, and it was shown that at the examination-before-trial he testified he made a *medial* approach (which would have been, medically, a better approach, and closer to the operative site), but when later shown the hospital record, he corrected himself to say it was a "posterior-lateral" approach.

I asked him about the scar he had found, the one that was one-half inch in diameter and about one inch away from the bone itself:

Q. Now, Doctor, you assumed that the ulnar nerve was contained in that scar?

A. Yes.

Q. Did you ever see this ulnar nerve, any part of it, from the time you opened up this man's elbow until the time you closed it up after the operation?

A. No, I did not.

Q. Did you at any time *identify* the ulnar nerve?

A. You mean by opening up the scar?

Q. By looking at it, seeing it?

A. No, I couldn't identify it. It wasn't in evidence. It wasn't there. It wasn't a normal joint. I knew where it was but I couldn't identify it separately.

Q. Now, Doctor, were you also asked this question: "Q. It is a fact, is it not, that in the course of this operative procedure, the procedure that you were performing, at no time did you visualize, see or identify the ulnar nerve?"

A. Yes.

Q. And did you give those answers?

A. I did.

Q. And, of course, Doctor, finding the scar as you described and the ulnar nerve not in its normal position and away from its normal position, that is an abnormal finding, isn't it?

A. Yes.

Q. Is there one word, Doctor, in your operative report on this operation which describes the scar that you have just testified to of the fact that the ulnar nerve was abnormally located, one word in your operative report, Doctor?

A. No, there wasn't.

The witness explained that the reason he had not observed the ulnar nerve in its regular groove was that *there must have been a previous nerve transplant* and that therefore it had been moved out of the groove. He was wrong. There had never been a previous transplant of the nerve and there was no reason for it not to be in its proper place—*if the doctor had taken the trouble to look.*

Q. Is it your testimony that this scar as you observed it, was due to the fact that a nerve transplant had been done on this ulnar nerve sometime before he came to you?

A. I assumed that was the case because he had had an arthroplasty. The physician never gave me an answer when I wrote to him as to what he did, so I don't know.

Q. If he did a transplant of the ulnar nerve, that is an important procedure, is it not?

A. If he had done it, yes.

Q. I mean, if the doctor did a nerve transplant, that would be a reported operative procedure, is that correct?

A. Yes, but I didn't do it.

Q. You say you had nothing to do with it; you say it was done previously?

A. I don't know whether it was or it wasn't. I *assumed* that it was.

Q. Well, you saw evidence of a nerve transplant? Isn't that your testimony?

A. I saw evidence of a scar which I *assumed* carried the nerve. I didn't see the nerve. I have testified to that a number of times.

Q. Doctor, I am not asking you about seeing the nerve. I ask you now about the fact that you said this man had had a previous nerve transplant. Isn't that what your answer was, Doctor?

A. I said that I assumed that he had. I didn't say he did, because I don't know. I don't know to this day whether he did or he didn't. It was never reported to me.

Q. Well, Doctor, it would be important to see, for example, if we could locate the hospital records of fifteen or sixteen years ago, to see what they did at that time. That would be important, wouldn't it?

A. It would be helpful.

Q. It would be helpful in knowing whether or not a previous nerve transplant was done?

A. It would.

The fifteen-year-old hospital records had, indeed, been located. They were on microfilm, and I had arranged for them to be enlarged so they could be placed in evidence. They proved conclusively that there had never been a previous nerve transplant. Dr. Winston looked carefully at the records, and finally agreed.

I now continued to question the doctor on the subject of the operation, seeking to establish that the doctor had removed a piece of bone on the *medial* side, the same side on which the ulnar nerve (which had not been identified or isolated) is located. My purpose was to show that the surgery was in close proximity to the nerve that had been injured.

Q. Doctor, coming back to the operation that you did on July 10, there came a time after you opened the joint, in the course of your operative procedure, that you removed a portion of this olecranon process?

A. Right.

Q. Now, in removing it, did you have to use a chisel?

A. Yes.

Q. And did you also have to use a hammer or mallet?

A. Yes.

Q. And in order to remove it did you have to apply force, applying a mallet to this?

A. Yes, gentle force.

Q. You say "gentle force," but force, in any event, to remove the bone?

A. Yes.

Q. Actually, you had to *chop* out a piece of bone, isn't that what you had to do, Doctor?

A. It's another way of stating it.

Q. Now, Doctor, was any portion of this bone, this hook that he had on the upper end of his ulna, or what you call the olecranon process—was any part of this bone mass which was giving him trouble, was any part on the *medial* side, the side nearest to where the ulnar nerve is located?

A. It extended across from lateral to medial, but the bone at that place is very narrow, so that the medial surface of the elbow is further over. You see, it goes to a point at that point.

Q. Let me read to you, Doctor, from your own hospital record as to where this mass was located: "On opening the joint, large quantities of rice bodies were exposed from the tip of the olecranon and the projecting *medial mass was removed*." So, Doctor, was the mass described by you not on the posterior side, but did you refer to it in your report as the "projecting *medial* mass." Are those the very words you used?

A. Yes.

Q. Without any words of posterior or side or anything else—

A. That's right.

Q. But "projecting *medial* mass"?

A. Correct, correct.

The picture was now becoming clearer. Although the doctor had made his incisional approach on the posterior-lateral side of the elbow, the piece of bone that he had to remove by force was on the medial side, the side closest to the body, the side where the ulnar nerve is located.

There remained but one or two important questions to ask:

Q. Doctor, is it good medical practice in the course of doing an operation such as you performed, to avoid injury to the ulnar nerve?

A. Of course.

Q. And contrariwise, is it bad medical practice, improper medical practice to injure—for a surgeon to injure the ulnar nerve during the course of such an operation?

A. Well, of course.

I felt that I had obtained some strong, if reluctant, admissions from the doctor. The plaintiff rested, and then the defense was called to its proof.

The patient, Larry Enright, made a fairly good witness, describing his abilities as a bowler and golfer, before and after Dr. Winston's operation, and carefully outlining his meeting with the doctor, the operation, the complaints he had made about pains in his fingers, the subsequent operations, and his present condition.

Then Dr. Harvey Fabricant, Chief of Orthopedics at several hospitals, was called. Dr. Fabricant testified that when he first saw the patient, about five weeks after the repair attempted by Dr. Winston, Enright presented the picture of a "typical ulnar nerve palsy." He further stated that when he performed a repair of the torn ulnar nerve two weeks later, the two ends of the nerve were separated by as much as one inch when he opened the elbow—and that they were in the ulnar groove. He affirmed that he had found no evidence of any previous nerve transplant.

Under direct examination, the doctor was then asked when,

in his opinion, with a reasonable degree of medical certainty, the injury to the ulnar nerve had occurred. Dr. Fabricant stated unequivocally that it had occurred at the time Dr. Winston performed his arthroplasty on Enright's elbow. The questioning continued in this fashion:

> Q. Doctor, in your opinion, is it good medical practice in the performance of an arthroplasty of the elbow to injure the ulnar nerve?
> A. No, sir.
> Q. Doctor, what is the accepted and proper practice insofar as the ulnar nerve is concerned?
> A. In such an operative procedure, all vital structures in the area involved should be identified and protected, including the ulnar nerve.
> Q. Doctor, is it good medical practice not to? I want you to assume that the ulnar nerve was not specifically identified at the time the arthroplasty was performed on July 10, 1961. Is that good medical practice?
> A. No, sir.
> Q. I want you to assume that it has been testified here by the surgeon who did the operation that what he observed at the time when he got into the joint was scar tissue approximately one half inch in diameter which he assumed to contain the ulnar nerve. Assuming that was so, is it good acceptable medical practice to assume where the ulnar nerve is located?
> A. No, sir.
> Q. If it has not been identified and protected, what may happen?
> A. *What happened here.*

Though Dr. Fabricant had been a convincing and helpful witness on direct examination, a few of the questions my opponent asked him proved to be embarrassing to Enright's case.

He showed that the history, as recorded by the *resident* who examined the patient at Andover Hospital, merely contained complaints about the elbow; there was *no mention made about the hand*. Also, the report on the examination of the patient by the resident spoke only of the elbow; there was no finding of a "claw" hand. Apparently, as is the case in most private hospitals, the private patient of Dr. Fabricant was only superficially questioned and examined by the resident.

On redirect examination, I tried to clarify the issue by asking Dr. Fabricant whether, when he saw Enright in his office for the first time, there was any question that he showed evidence of ulnar nerve palsy. The doctor affirmed that there was absolutely no question about it in his opinion: he had recorded it in his records for that day, and had admitted him to the hospital for precisely that reason—to explore the ulnar nerve.

Our final witness was Dr. Leonard Bruen, who had subsequently treated Larry Enright; he too testified that it was bad practice to injure the ulnar nerve when performing an arthroplasty of the elbow joint.

The defense then rested.

When the gauntlet was thrown back to the plaintiff, he called as a medical expert Dr. Stanley Bienenstock, who had excellent qualifications as an orthopedic surgeon. He had recently returned from Vietnam, where he had been doing work at one of Tom Dooley's hospitals as an orthopedic specialist.

Dr. Bienenstock testified that he had reviewed a number of the hospital records and depositions given by Dr. Winston, and that he had found no departure from good medical practice.

In cross-examining this doctor, there could be no attack on his qualifications. But bias or prejudice is always a possibility, and, though I had no intimations that a friendship between Dr. Winston and Dr. Bienenstock existed, I decided to try that tact first. The hunch was correct. The two doctors had

met a full thirty-five years earlier, and though they had not
seen each other since Dr. Winston had moved from New
York to Washington, D.C., the former knew when he was
consulted for his opinion in this case that it involved a doctor
he knew personally. The admission was a valuable one, but it
was not enough. The doctor had to be questioned on the central medical problem: that you must *identify* the ulnar nerve
before you go about cutting off any bone that is on the same
medial side. The doctor started to fence:

Q. Doctor, is it a correct statement that in doing an
arthroplasty on the elbow of a patient, first it is of the
utmost importance that the ulnar nerve be identified?

A. What do you mean by "identified." Just tell me
exactly what you mean and I will answer your question.

Q. Doctor Bienenstock, is the word "identified" used
by doctors in referring to an operation performed—an
arthroplasty. Did you ever hear that term before?

A. Of course I have.

Q. I will accept your understanding of what the term
means. Do you have any trouble with that term, Doctor?

A. Not in the least.

Q. So, accepting your term of what your understanding of what "identitfy" means, is it accepted and proper
medical practice that in doing an arthroplasty involving
the elbow joint that a *cardinal rule* is that the ulnar nerve
must be identified?

A. You must know where the ulnar nerve is.

Q. Well, you might *guess* where it is, right, Doctor? Is
that good practice?

A. That would not be good practice.

Q. You might *think* where it is. Would that be good
practice?

A. That would be acceptable in certain circumstances,
yes.

q. Would you agree that the safe acceptable practice is to *visualize* the ulnar nerve?

a. In certain circumstances that would be the best procedure, yes.

q. So if you were to open up an elbow joint and to notice that where the ulnar groove is there is scar tissue there, you would assume that the ulnar nerve must be contained within that scar tissue?

a. That's correct, unless I knew that someone else had moved it out of that area.

q. In other words, unless you knew there had been a transplant?

a. That's right.

q. You would have to know that?

a. Definitely.

q. That is a major procedure—a transplant?

a. It is a big procedure.

q. And if you didn't know there had been a transplant or you hadn't been told or seen a record telling you there had been a transplant, you certainly wouldn't assume there was one?

a. *I would assume there was none.*

The doctor also finally agreed that if you do not see the ulnar nerve in its regular groove, and simply see scar tissue adjacent to it, you cannot assume that the ulnar nerve is in the scar tissue: you must check it out.

q. All you see is scar tissue about an inch away from the ulnar groove, no nerve, and the scar tissue is about a half inch in diameter. Visualize it now.

a. Yes.

q. Given the situation, Doctor, wouldn't you, as good medical practice, probe further to ascertain where the ulnar nerve is?

A. I would presume that the ulnar nerve was in that scar tissue.

Q. Would you check it out, Doctor? Would you check it above or below the scar which is only a half inch?

A. *If there were only a half inch of scar tissue running lengthwise, I would, yes.*

Q. In other words, then, Doctor, do you agree that if the scar is only a half inch in diameter and lengthwise— that good medical practice would be what? Would you check it above? How would you do it, Dr. Bienenstock?

A. Well, I would look for the ulnar nerve along its usual course above and below the site of the pathology.

Q. And if you saw it then you would—

A. *I would track it down.*

Q. In other words, Doctor, as good medical practice you would track that nerve down above or below this scar. That is good practice?

A. Yes.

Q. The reason being, Doctor, that in performing this kind of operation, care must be taken not to injure the nerve?

A. That is correct.

Q. Actually, Doctor, the purpose of the identification, of knowing whether the nerve is in its groove or any-where else, is to make sure that it is out of the *field of operation.*

A. That is absolutely correct.

Q. That is of paramount importance?

A. Absolutely.

Q. Because you want to make sure not to injure the ulnar nerve; is that right.

A. Yes, sir.

Q. Because, if you injure the ulnar nerve, the patient will develop an ulnar palsy.

A. That is correct.

Though I had now gained a major admission from the doctor, I still had to show that he was wrong in assuming that the operation was being done on the *lateral* and not the *medial* side. Obviously, if corrective surgery to a bone was to be performed on the lateral side, it would be so far removed from the ulnar nerve located on the opposite side that you would not have to concern yourself with it. Further questioning drew Dr. Bienenstock's admission that if the operation were purely confined to the lateral side of the joint, the ulnar nerve would be of no concern. I reiterated the doctor's former testimony that if "the operation were to include any part of the medial side," he would *"want to make sure where that ulnar nerve is located."* Dr. Bienenstock affirmed this: yes, he would want to protect it.

The final point we sought to show through this expert was that he had never seen the important records of the Andover Hospital, and had never seen the admission history. I began by reading the "Admission Note" written by Dr. Fabricant, and duly signed by him, on the day of Enright's admission to the hospital.

Q. "Two and a half months ago an attempt at the revision of the arthroplasty was carried out elsewhere. Following this surgical procedure, patient relates that his arm was mobilized in extension and *immediately postoperatively began to complain of numbness of the ring and small fingers.* When seen in the office was most recently within the past week, patient demonstrates a *typical ulnar nerve palsy* involving the adductor thumb muscles and lateral interossei."

Doctor, assuming those facts with reasonable medical certainty, *would it be fair to say that the palsy that is described here occurred at the time of the operation on July 10, 1961?*

A. *If those facts are so, I will say yes.*

The plaintiff's last witness was a surprise to the jury. They had subpoenaed to the stand Mrs. Enright, the defendant's wife, and showed that when she and her husband returned to New York from Washington, following the operation by Dr. Winston, she had written a letter to the doctor telling him that she wished he could have seen the look of pleasure on their son's face when he saw that his father's arms were now the same length. The boy had said, "This doctor must be a genius," Mrs. Enright had written in the letter; and she had added, "and we agree."

The best I could do was to show that the letter had been written the day after she arrived in New York and that it represented a kind of "bread and butter" letter, sent to show appreciation. At the time she wrote it, she probably believed that, as Dr. Winston had stated, the condition of the hand would clear up. Unfortunately, it never did.

Both sides then rested, and each side prepared to sum up.

As counsel for the defense, I presented my summation first.

"The main question is," I began, "did the ulnar nerve palsy develop because of the operation performed by Dr. Winston?" I stressed that it was accepted good medical practice that the nerve be identified—but that Dr. Winston had only "assumed" or "guessed" that it was in the scar tissue he claimed to have seen. "The doctor's explanation for not seeing the nerve in its regular groove is that there must have been a *previous* transplant or removal of the nerve. We now know that never took place. In fact, Dr. Fabricant tells us that when he did the repair on the nerve six weeks after the operation by Dr. Winston, although he found the nerve dissected or cut, *it was still in its regular groove.*"

I went on to show how Dr. Winston insisted that the post-operative care was uneventful—with no complaints about any trouble with fingers. But where were the doctor's office records?

Admittedly, he, like every doctor, kept records of the

patient's *complaints* and his *findings* on these many visits of the patient to the doctor's office.

Well, now you see them, now you don't. Remember the doctor's story of how he had seen those records in his office only this past Sunday? They were one or two pages and he would bring them to court. Have you seen them? I haven't. Does it have the ring of truth? Is the doctor performing "abracadabra" for you?

In your search for the truth you have a right to expect a certain amount of candor and fairness from each side. A lawsuit is not a game of wits with one side trying to outsmart the other and presenting some of the proof while hiding the rest under the table.

I say to you that the reason those office records were not produced is because they would prove the truthfulness of the patient's story. It is like an octopus who emits a dark, inky fluid, hoping to produce enough confusion and muddy waters to escape unnoticed.

Concerning Dr. Bienenstock, I stressed that he had never examined the patient, and had rendered his opinion solely on records that were submitted to him; these did not include those of the Andover Hospital. Furthermore, Dr. Bienenstock was under the mistaken opinion that since the opening incision was on the *outside*, then that was where the operation itself must have been performed. "Of course," I noted, "if the operation was to be on the outside, you would not have to 'identify' or worry about the ulnar nerve, which is way over on the inside. But we know the bone that had to be removed with a mallet and chisel *was* on the inside, right smack where the ulnar nerve is located."

I reviewed Larry Enright's testimony concerning the pain and difficulty he had had with his hand in Washington; noted that the Andover Hospital Record recorded the patient's complaints, as well as Dr. Fabricant's findings of a torn ulnar nerve that he had to repair by operative procedure; and then recalled the testimony of Dr. Leonard Bruen, who had described the complication as a "classical" picture that follows injury to the nerve.

Finally, I stressed this:

> You know, in a courtroom things have a way of getting out of focus. I'm sure this must have occurred to you. Isn't it peculiar that this ulnar nerve palsy should develop shortly after the operation done by Dr. Winston? Is it a mere coincidence?
>
> We know the ulnar nerve was severed. *Who did it?* Has Dr. Winston or his expert friend, Dr. Bienenstock, offered any explanation? I haven't heard any.
>
> If you think that Dr. Winston had nothing to do with the complications that developed, say so. But, if logic and reason mean anything, your verdict will be for the patient.

My opponent, Sherman Bernhardt, then followed me. He had the last say, and I had no opportunity to answer his arguments. He came up with a real haymaker.

> Sure, the patient developed a lacerated ulnar nerve, but not from the operation of Dr. Winston. Remember the resident's admission notes and physical examination at the Andover Hospital? Not a word about any problem with the hand or fingers. Not a finding of any "claw" hand. Would he have overlooked such an important condition, especially since that was the very reason the patient went into the hospital?

And he went on:

> Kramer wants to know where the injury to the nerve occurred? I'll tell him. At Andover Hospital by Dr. Fabricant. *He is the culprit.*

Apparently the jury took the bait. Bernhardt had created enough doubt in the minds of some of the jurors, and after deliberating for hours they reported to Judge Nadel that they were deadlocked. The judge had no choice but to dismiss the jury and order a new trial.

Of course, my client and I were very disappointed. We had put in as good a case as we ever hoped to, and yet could not persuade ten of the twelve jurors. It had been an expensive and time-consuming trial.

Several months later the case again came to trial, but this time we were more fully prepared. Knowing how effective Sherman Bernhardt's argument had been in casting blame from Dr. Winston to Dr. Fabricant, I subpoenaed the "operative log" of Andover Hospital. Every hospital must keep in its operating room a book containing certain data relevant to operations performed at the hospital. It is kept by the operating *nurse*, not the doctor. Included in the data is the "preoperative diagnosis" and the "postoperative diagnosis." This clearly showed that the "preoperative diagnosis" was "to explore the ulnar nerve" and that the postoperative diagnosis was "repair and transplant of the ulnar nerve." This proved unequivocally that before the operation the ulnar nerve was already implicated and that Dr. Fabricant had nothing to do with injuring it; it had already been damaged by Dr. Winston.

In my new summation, I added a compelling argument to persuade the jury that the negligent doctor was indeed Dr. Winston and not Dr. Fabricant:

> The one person who knows what the condition of his hand was on admission to the Andover Hospital is *the patient*, Larry Enright. He knows whether he had it before or after the operation performed by Dr. Fabricant. If Dr. Fabricant was the culprit, do you think for a moment that Enright would have hesitated to sue *him*? In fact, one of the problems with the case was that the pa-

tient could not get jurisdiction of Dr. Winston because he was a nonresident. Why should the patient blame an innocent nonresident doctor when right in New York City he had the negligent doctor?

This time the jury dismissed the claim of Dr. Winston for his medical bill, and rendered a verdict for the patient in his counterclaim—in the sum of $48,000. This was an unusual verdict in the Civil Court, since it is a court of limited jurisdiction and damage awards on counterclaims are rarely seen in that sum.

But the award was modest when measured in the light of the irreparable damage done to the patient.

X

THE CARELESS SCALPEL

A gynecological case—a hysterectomy with damage
to the bladder and resultant urinary leakage

In any major operative procedure many surgical instruments are used. To name just a few, there are *retractors*, to hold open the lips of a wound; *clamps*, to compress a part; *hemostats*, to stop bleeding; and, what is perhaps the most important instrument of all, the scalpel—a straight knife. The success or failure of the operation will frequently depend upon the judicious use of these tools.

The primary objective of surgery, as in every branch of medicine, is to cure and restore the patient to health. In performing an operation, there are certain basic qualifications that the surgeon must possess, and certain tenets he must follow:

1. He must possess *operative skill;*
2. he must be *gentle* in the handling of tissues;
3. he must possess *dextrous* fingers;
4. he must *avoid undue haste;*
5. he must have an intimate knowledge of *anatomy*.

It is interesting to reflect that Hippocrates, the Father of Medicine, knew little, if anything, about anatomy. One of his principal contributions was actually that he was the first to rebel against the idea that all sickness was caused by "angry gods." He believed that illness came from earthly causes, and thus became the first to separate medicine from superstition and to give it a scientific approach.

Actually, it was not until almost six hundred years later, in the second century A.D., when Claudius Galen began to dissect animals, particularly apes, that anatomy first began to be understood. But Galen mistakenly believed that the anatomy and bodily function of ape and man were identical, and he also thought that blood formed in the liver, flowed through the body, and ended up in the heart.

This concept prevailed until 1628, when William Harvey published his famous *Dissertation Concerning the Motion of the Heart and Blood in Animals*, proving that it was the other way around.

It remained for Andreas Vesalius, in the sixtenth century, to attempt the first autopsy of a human body, and it was he who advanced the "shocking" proposal that much could be learned from this procedure. When in 1543 he published *The Working of the Human Body*, medicine was finally on the road to its intimate understanding of the greatest miracle of all: the human body.

Yet it should be noted that even today, despite all the progress that has been made in medicine, there are parts of the body that still remain a mystery. For example, a portion of the brain is still referred to as the "silent area," not because it serves no purpose, but because as yet its precise function has not been revealed.

All this is preliminary to my presentation of a case involving an all-too-frequent operative procedure known as a *hysterectomy* (removal of the uterus or womb). To be successfully executed, this operation requires an intimate understanding of anatomy. Without it, there can be the direst of results.

However, in many instances in which a hysterectomy has actually been performed, it has been shown that no operation was necessary. In 1958, the New York State Department of Health and the New York Department of Insurance appointed a commission to study hospital and medical care in the state. The commission was headed by Dr. Ray E. Trussell, who conducted an extensive survey. In the report of their findings, published in 1962, they had this to say about hysterectomies:

A hysterectomy had been performed on sixty patients in the sample. From a review of the records, including the operative report and the pathology findings, the surveyor felt that *one-third were operated on unnecessarily and that some question could be raised about the advisability of the operation in another 10 percent of the cases.* At the very least, these women should have had a dilation and curettage (scraping of the uterus), followed by a period of observation prior to the hysterectomy. *In many instances, the dilation and curettage alone would have alleviated the symptoms.*

When we realize that about 300,000 hysterectomies are done each year, it would appear that 100,000 of these operations may have been unnecessary. The women involved thus might have been spared not only the amputation of their womb, with all its consequences—both physical and mental—but also from the many complications that are so prevalent in major surgery, such as infection, hemorrhage, hepatitis, embolism, and cardiac arrest.

If the utmost care is not exercised, there is a special complication peculiar to the removal of the uterus, and that is *surgical injury to its adjoining organ, the bladder;* a vesicovaginal fistula may be created ("vesico" means bladder, and a fistula is an abnormal hole or opening), with resulting urinary leakage and all its dreadful effects.

Such was the case in a hysterectomy performed on Miss Jane Harriman.

Miss Harriman was fifty-two years old, unmarried, and had worked for a large corporation for thirty years. At fifty she had retired on a small pension and was in general good health, except that she had developed a *frequency of menstrual flow*. As a result she went to see Dr. Walter Deluca, a specialist in women's diseases. After examination, Dr. Deluca found that Miss Harriman had some fibroids, or growths, on her uterus, and he advised that a hysterectomy be performed.

She agreed, and on June 15, 1959, at the Wittenborn Hospital in Manhattan, the doctor performed the operative procedure—removal of the uterus. In addition, as is often done at this operation, he also removed her ovaries.

The operation was routine and uncomplicated, but a few days later the patient developed urinary leakage. It was then discovered that she had a vesico-vaginal fistula, an abnormal opening in her bladder. Since the function of the bladder is to store urine until enough collects to be eliminated, if there is a fistula in it the urine will leak out prematurely—with all its embarrassing effects. Miss Harriman thereafter underwent several operative procedures to repair the fistula. The final one was successful.

Miss Harriman was a timid soul who was very reluctant to sue the doctor—or anyone else, for that matter. But after she had used up her life savings on hospital and doctors' bills, she finally decided to consult an attorney.

An action was started in malpractice against Dr. Deluca in the Supreme Court of New York County. After completion of all the preliminary proceedings—including the important examination-before-trial of the parties—the case was reached for trial in 1962, before the Honorable Vincent A. Lupiano and a jury.

The trial lawyer for the defendant, Dr. Deluca, was Tom Costello, who so impressed me with the way he handled the defense that, some time later, I invited him to join my firm. He remained with us until quite recently, when he joined another law firm in order to pursue his first love—the defense of cases.

The opening statements of the lawyers are usually not recorded unless there is a specific request. My opponent so requested, and we then delivered our openings.

In my opening, I outlined our case carefully to the jury. We would prove that

1. the hysterectomy performed on Miss Harriman was in and of itself a normal, uncomplicated, run-of-the-mill operative procedure;

2. that a surgeon should avoid injury to the bladder when he performs a hysterectomy; he should not nick it, injure it, get a suture into it, put his clamps upon it, or press too hard on it;

3. and that if good surgical technique is adopted, you simply do not get, will not get, and should not get, a fistula of the bladder.

Having completed my remarks, my opponent, Tom Costello, then stated what he would prove. He said in part:

The defense in this case will show that one of the *hazards* of surgery of this nature is the development or the occurrence of a vesico-vaginal fistula. No matter what surgery is performed, there are hazards to all types of surgery. Hemorrhage, for example, is one of the hazards of any type of surgery, and a vesico-vaginal fistula is a hazard of surgery; and the testimony will show that it is a hazard to be avoided; but we will show in this case, and what the case is going to come down to as far as the proof is concerned, is what is the standard of medicine practiced here in the State of New York.

We will show that Dr. Deluca performed his operation strictly in accordance with the standards of medicine as practiced here in the State of New York.

We will show that it is not true that merely because a

fistula develops as a complication of a hysterectomy, that that development or complication was caused by some carelessness or deficiency or deviation by Dr. Deluca, even though that complication is a rare complication in hysterectomy operations.

In other words, we will show that you can have excellent procedure, excellent medical procedure, the operation can be performed perfectly and this complication can still develop. We will show further, and we will do this by expert testimony, that there are other causes of a fistula developing other than some deviation or carelessness on the part of the doctor who is performing the operation.

For example, in the course of an operation of this nature it is necessary to cut off certain blood vessels, to tie them off, because there is a separation, for example, of the uterine vessels. The uterus is removed. Ligaments must be cut and tied off. Vessels must be cut and tied off. And as a result of this procedure, there is a lack of blood supply to the area involved, and of course the bladder is in close proximity to where this actual operation takes place.

Now, as a result of this vascularization process, a necrosis will develop. For example, a portion of the bladder, because of a lack of blood supply, can lose something that it had before, can die off, certain cells die off, and a fistula will develop because of the lack of blood supply in that particular area.

And during the course of the trial, we will develop other reasons and causes as to how a fistula can develop other than as a result of the surgery that took place.

It was an impressive opening—and we knew we would have a genuine battle on our hands, though we were convinced there had indeed been malpractice.

The plaintiff's case was then presented in short order. I called Miss Harriman, who recited the facts as given above.

Though she was obviously frightened by the formality of the trial, all in all she made a good witness.

Then the examination-before-trial of Dr. Deluca was read, and I called as an expert Dr. George Blaise, a urologist who testified that in doing a hysterectomy the bladder should *not* have been injured:

Q. Well, Doctor, you say that the bladder is kept away from the field of operation. What do you mean by that, Doctor?

A. Simply that one does not want to injure an adjoining organ when doing any kind of surgery, and in removing a uterus, the bladder is close to that, as are the intestines; and one avoids the intestines, one avoids the bladder and any contiguous structures as well.

Q. Doctor, when a hysterectomy is performed, is the bladder itself any part of the operative procedure?

A. It is not.

Q. Doctor, then, in your opinion with a reasonable degree of medical certainty, was a hysterectomy which results in an involvement of this adjoining organ, the bladder, results in an abnormal opening into it, was it done in the accepted and proper medical manner?

MR. COSTELLO. I object, your Honor.

THE COURT. Overruled.

A. If a vescio-vaginal fistula develops, an abnormality of urinary drainage, there then must be injury to the bladder to occasion the formation of that abnormal opening.

In cross-examination of the witness the defense tried to show that the fistula could occur because of "devascularization," which means lack of blood supply to tissues, with their resultant damage, or because of *infection*.

On re-direct examination, I tried to clear up the points raised by Tom Costello:

Q. Doctor, the devascularization we are talking about, so we get it clear, pertains to what area or what organ?

A. The base of the bladder.

Q. All right. And, Doctor, in the course of the operative procedure, if it has been done properly, should there be any devascularization of the base of the bladder?

A. No.

Q. What is the reason for that, Doctor?

A. The reason for the devascularization may be that a clamp is placed across the bladder tissue or that some of the tissue from the bladder is included in one of the sutures, and the blood vessels are compromised.

Q. Doctor, you have been asked about uterine ligaments and vessels and blood vessels being tied off. Are there any vessels or ligaments of the bladder that are disturbed in any way in this operative procedure?

A. Normally, no.

Q. Then if the procedure is done properly, those, the ligaments and blood vessels as relate to the bladder, should not be disturbed?

A. That is correct.

Q. In so far as this question of *infection*, Doctor, was she given routinely, as in every hysterectomy, or operative procedure, antibiotics for a few days postoperative?

A. Yes.

Q. As a matter of fact, is that ordered preoperatively, Doctor?

A. Sometimes it may be ordered before operation.

Q. If she had any infection evident on the 18th, 19th or 20th or any of the subsequent days, would she, as part of the hospital procedure, have been given antibiotics then?

A. Yes.

Q. Doctor, is there any evidence in the hospital record that she had any infection postoperative?

A. No.

Q. In your opinion with a reasonable degree of medical certainty, did infection have anything to do with the subsequent development of the fistula?

A. *No.*

The case for the plaintiff was in, and I rested.

Many times the motion to dismiss that is made at this juncture by the defense attorney is perfunctory. But my opponent argued strenuously this time, and at great length, that we had failed to make out a case because we did not prove the precise cause of the fistula, and furthermore, because my expert, Dr. Blaise, had agreed that it is one of the "hazards" of the surgery.

At the completion of Tom Costello's argument, the court asked, "Mr. Kramer, do you wish to respond?"

I had to respond—otherwise our case might be lost. I began:

If I may, with your Honor's permission. First, to answer the first point that is made, that there was no evidence of deviation from accepted medical practice: The proof was by Dr. Blaise that the bladder is an adjoining organ just like the intestines are and in no way should be involved or compromised in this procedure, and, in fact, the doctor clearly pointed out that in his opinion the fistula which developed in this case, in this adjoining organ, was caused by one of three things: either a clamp, a ligature or a suture, any one of which is a departure from accepted practice by reason of the fact that the bladder should not be in any way touched or compromised, injured in the course of this procedure.

Now, mention has been made of the *Majorka v. St. Catherine's Hospital* case which was tried before Judge Beckinella. I am familiar with the case, your Honor, and I may say to your Honor that that case is a far cry from this one for this reason: In that case we were dealing with a situation where the defendant was doing a cutdown in preparing the child's leg for intravenous, and in the course of it being done, an infection set in at the site where the cutdown was performed. And the court could well point out there, as Judge Beckinella did, that in that situation there was no proof of any deviation.

Here we have an entirely different situation, your Honor, because the organ which was injured should not have been involved or touched either by a clamp, ligature or suture of any kind, and consequently the Majorka case is in no way relevant.

I may say too, in passing, that I tried exactly this type of case, and frankly not as good, before Judge Beckinella, where Dr. Blaise was a witness, and the court denied the motion to dismiss at the end of the plaintiff's case.

Then this question of infection is raised. It is true, I think the evidence has now clearly indicated Dr. Blaise has said it and even from the examination-before-trial of the defendant himself, that infection played no role whatsoever in the causation of this fistula; plus, of course, the fact that there was no infection.

And finally, your Honor, the point is made that a vesicle-vaginal fistula, and Dr. Blaise agreed to it, is a hazard of a hysterectomy, and that is true. But it is a hazard, your Honor, in the same way that I, as a passenger in an airplane, undergo the hazard that the plane may crash; or I, as a driver or a passenger in an automobile, undergo the hazard that the automobile may be in an accident.

Now, there is a distinction between hazards which are preventable and hazards which are unavoidable.

The proof in this case, and the analogy again of the plane crash, there are plane crashes which occur for which there is no apparent cause—act of God or unavoidable. On the other hand, there are crashes which occur—even there it is one of the hazards—where there has been either pilot error or error in the maintenance of the plane.

And so I submit to your Honor that the other arguments my friend makes are arguments to be made to the jury. That is a question of fact for the jury to determine. That is going to be their final decision, as to whether or not this operation, even though done technically correctly —we have no quarrel with the technique employed. It is in the *execution* of the technique that we have reason to quarrel, and so I submit, your Honor, that the plaintiff has made out a prima facie case.

After I had made this lengthy reply, I breathed a sigh of relief when the court announced, "Decision reserved."

The defense now had to come forward with their proof. It is my theory that more cases are actually won by plaintiffs in the defendant's handling of the case than in their own. In effect, when you are putting in your own proof, it is the defendant's innings, because he has a chance to take it apart. It is not until you get an opportunity to cross-examine the defendant's witness that your case begins to gain momentum. In this case, Tom Costello must have recognized the special truth in this theory—and had thus tried to terminate the trial early.

Dr. Deluca, the defendant, was called as the first witness for the defense. He testified as to his extensive qualifications as a gynecologist; the necessity for the operation; the technique he used; and to the fact that he did not injure the bladder during the course of the operation. The direct examination was concise and to the point.

I had given a great deal of thought to the points I wanted to develop in my cross-examination of Dr. Deluca. I felt that it was important to show that the hysterectomy he performed on Miss Harriman was run-of-the-mill and that he encountered no complications. But the doctor did not give in easily:

Q. Now, this operation, this hysterectomy that you

performed on Miss Harriman, that is a fairly common-place type of operation in women who are, let us say, past fifty years of age?

A. Yes, sir.

Q. And I suppose, Doctor, that some of them are pretty complicated, where, for example, it involves a malignancy or abnormally large fibroids?

A. Yes, sir.

Q. On the other hand, Doctor, some of the procedures are uncomplicated and routine—is that correct?

A. I think they are all treated with respect, sir.

Q. I didn't say not, Doctor. Of course, they are. But I say some of these procedures by virtue of the condition that exists, a person, say, with malignancy of the uterus represents one type of picture, as distinguished from a woman who has the average-size uterus or fibroids; isn't that true?

A. Yes, sir.

Q. Now, in this case, in Miss Harriman's case, Doctor, would it be fair to say that the operation you performed was a run-of-the-mill, with no complications?

A. I don't think any complete hysterectomy is a run-of-the-mill anything.

Q. I am talking as a hysterectomy procedure, did you find that this was a run-of-the-mill procedure, as far as you were concerned? Can you answer that question, Doctor?

A. Sir, I never use that term in surgery.

Q. Doctor, let me ask you this: Do you recall testifying at an examination-before-trial back in June of 1960, which would be about a year after the operation was performed and about two and a half years ago?

A. Yes.

Q. Your testimony at that time under oath. Do you remember being asked this question and giving this answer?

"Q. Did you find any complications as you performed it?

"A. No.

"Q. In other words, Doctor, as far as you were concerned this was the *run-of-the-mill hysterectomy?*

"A. *Yes.*"

Do you remember being asked those questions and giving those answers at the time?

THE COURT. Did you give that answer to that question, Doctor?

THE WITNESS. *I did.*

I then wanted to show that the growths or fibroids were actually small or insignificant and that there was no cancer:

Q. Doctor, so that there is no question about it, when you saw her prior to the operation, would it be fair to say that what she had insofar as the uterus was concerned was *slight* enlargement of the uterus? Would that be a fair description of it?

A. Yes, sir.

Q. Postoperative it is routine, of course, as practiced at this hospital, that when a hysterectomy is done the portions of the body that you have removed have to be sent to the laboratory for gross and microscopic analysis, and that was done here?

A. Yes, sir.

Q. Doctor, is it correct to say that first of all on microscopic and gross analysis it was determined that there was no malignancy involved in this case?

A. Yes, sir.

Q. Was it also determined that these growths or fibroids that Miss Harriman had on her uterus, that they were *small* in nature?

A. Yes.

The time was now ripe to come to grips with the main claim that the defendant *caused the fistula*. An attempt to develop that was done as follows:

Q. Now, Doctor, when you perform a hysterectomy you, of course, use a knife, retractors, and a needle for suture—some of the instruments you use?

A. Yes.

Q. And used in this case?

A. Yes.

Q. And, of course, Doctor, in the use of these instruments you endeavor to avoid trauma to the bladder; is that correct?

A. Yes.

Q. So that we understand what we mean by the word trauma, *t-r-a-u-m-a*, that is a medical term for injury; is that correct?

A. Yes.

Q. Now, Dr. Deluca, you say that you made a diagnosis of a vesico-vaginal fistula on June 26th, eleven days postoperative; is that correct?

A. I believe it was on the 23rd.

Q. June 23rd, all right, eight days postoperative; is that correct?

A. Yes.

Q. *What caused it?*

A. *I am unable to answer that question.*

I was making progress. The fact that he did not know the cause of the fistula was a good answer for us, but I gambled with my next question, and it paid off:

Q. Could the hysterectomy that you performed have been the cause?

MR. COSTELLO. I am going to object to this question, your Honor. I object to the form of the question.

THE COURT. Overruled.

THE WITNESS. *Yes.*

I then decided to explore the specific way in which the operative procedure could have injured the bladder:

Q. Doctor, there is no question that the bladder should be pushed out of the way of the operative site?

A. Yes.

Q. Just as you mentioned earlier when you stated in the course of the procedure, you isolated the intestines and got that out of the way; isn't that correct?

A. Yes.

Q. The reason for that is to avoid injury, say to either the intestines or to the bladder?

A. Yes.

Q. Let me ask you this, Doctor: One of the ways in the course of your performance of the hysterectomy that the bladder may be injured is, for example, first of all by accidental incision or tearing of the bladder at the time of the operation.

A. Yes.

Q. And, Doctor, would another way be by a ligature or a suture causing necrosis in a small area of the bladder wall?

A. Yes.

Q. In other words, by coming accidentally in contact with it and causing the necrosis?

A. Yes.

The admissions were flowing like water. I decided to press on and show what *precautions* should be taken to avoid the injury:

Q. Now, Doctor, isn't it true that in the performance

of this procedure there are certain precautions that you, as a surgeon, should take in order to avoid injury to the bladder?

A. Yes.

Q. Could you name some of those precautions?

A. The first precaution is the bladder should be emptied before the operation starts. The second precaution is you must avoid trauma to the bladder.

Q. Doctor, is that your complete answer?

A. Yes, sir.

Q. How about the precaution that should be taken, Doctor, so that a proper cleavage is taken between the uterus and the bladder, a proper separation of the two; is that an important precaution?

A. Yes, sir.

Q. Is it also important when the cleavage is done that the bladder be pushed downward and out of place, out of danger?

A. Yes, sir.

Q. In the freeing of the bladder do you free the bladder, Doctor, from the vagina and the cervix?

A. Yes, to an extent.

Q. Must that be done with great care?

A. Yes, sir.

Q. The reason it must be done with great care, Doctor, is that you do not injure the bladder; is that correct?

A. Yes.

Q. Because if you do compromise it in any way it may result in a vesico-vaginal fistula?

A. Yes.

In my final attack on the witness I wanted to utilize all the medical research I had done. A malpractice case is challenging to the attorneys for both sides, but it is especially so for the plaintiff's lawyer. He must understand a subject for which he has had no training, and he must be prepared to cope with defense witnesses who are often outstanding experts.

Medical textbooks—as you have seen in earlier cases—are valuable points of reference in cross-examination, and are usually effective with the jury. The defendant had agreed that Dr. Henry Falk is an authority; in fact, Dr. Deluca had sent Miss Harriman to see Dr. Falk when she developed her fistula. My questioning of the witness continued as follows:

> Q. Doctor, isn't it true that the major cause of vesico-vaginal fistula is surgical trauma?
>
> A. Yes.
>
> Q. Doctor, do you agree with this statement contained in Dr. Falk's book under "surgical trauma": "In our series in the last 55 fistulas, 50 of them were due to surgical trauma."
>
> Do you agree with that, Doctor?
>
> A. I wouldn't know.
>
> Q. Let me ask you whether you agree with this statement by Dr. Falk: "If the bladder has not been displaced downward sufficiently it may be injured in the closure. A suture on the anterior cuff of the vagina for hemostasis—" the word "hemostasis," does that mean "preventing bleeding"?
>
> A. Yes.
>
> Q. "—may include the bladder wall and lead to subsequent necrosis and late fistula formation." Do you agree with that, Doctor?
>
> A. Yes.
>
> Q. In other words, what Dr. Falk is saying and what you agree to now, is that if the bladder hadn't been moved down sufficiently a suture that has been placed on the vagina wall, if it should include part of the bladder, may result in subsequent necrosis and late fistula—is that correct?

A. Yes, sir.

Q. Let me ask you this: Do you agree with this statement: "That during the freeing of the bladder from the vagina and cervix some small vessels to the bladder may be injured." The need for hemostasis "—by suture or clamping of these vessels close to the bladder wall is not infrequent. *This should be done with great care.* If too big a bite is taken, the procedure may result in necrosis and subsequent fistula formation which may not manifest itself until one to three weeks after surgery."

Isn't that true, Doctor?

A. Yes, sir.

Q. I have an article here entitled "Lower Urinary Tract Fistulas in Women. A Study based on 292 Cases," by Drs. Norman F. Miller and Harry George, from the Department of Obstetrics and Gynecology of the University of Michigan in Ann Arbor, Michigan. Well recognized, Doctor?

A. Yes.

Q. I want to ask you, Doctor, whether you agree with this statement: "Because pelvic surgery is today the major cause of urinary fistulas in women it is desirable to consider the question of why this is so. Doubtless unrecognized direct injury to the bladder occurring at the time of operation plays an etiological role. In this category we include such things as incision into or actual tearing of the bladder, incision of the ureter and similar trauma."

You agree thus far, Doctor, with what I have read?

A. Yes.

Q. This is one of the things we have talked about. That is where there is direct injury to the bladder by use of the instrument; is that correct?

A. You are quoting from that article?

Q. Yes.

A. Yes.

Q. "Unrecognized injuries are not common but probably occur during bladder mobilization or as a consequence of excessive force applied through improper or sharp bladder retraction."

Do you agree with that, Doctor?

A. It's possible.

Q. To continue, Doctor, do you agree with this statement?

"The late appearance of uncontrolled urinary leakage days or even weeks after operation suggests a different causative factor. In these late postoperative instances of uncontrolled urinary leakage it appears that a vascular necrosis plays an important role."

Do you agree with that, Doctor?

A. Yes.

Q. "This may occur secondary to the placement of suture material in the bladder or follow prolonged retractive pressure leading to trauma and subsequent necrosis of the affected area."

Do you agree with that statement, Doctor?

A. Yes.

Q. And finally, I am going to ask you, Doctor Deluca, whether you agree with this statement:

"Possibly we do not guard against this sort of injury as carefully as we should."

Do you agree with that statement, yes or no?

A. *No.*

Every trial lawyer has vanity—and I'm sure that I have my share. I had done my homework before the trial, and now felt it had paid off. The answers I had got from Dr. Deluca on cross-examination were more than I could have hoped for in my wildest dreams. I began to feel a sense of confidence. This was probably my first mistake, because ordinarily I am the world's worst pessimist as far as a trial goes.

As its last witness, the defense called Dr. William Eagan,

who had subsequently treated Miss Harriman, and asked him simply whether the operation, as reported, was done in accordance with good medical practice. I made the point that I did not quarrel with the doctor's technique, but with his *execution* of the technique. When Tom Costello had finished with the witness, I asked no questions in cross-examination.

The defense rested.

Tom Costello, in his summation, urged the same points he had made throughout the trial—namely, that the procedure was proper; that no evidence had been presented as to what caused the fistula; and that the complication can develop without fault.

When it came my turn to sum up, I dealt first with the burden of proof. I like to anticipate the judge's instructions to the jury. He will instruct them that the plaintiff has the burden of proving her case by a "fair preponderance" of the evidence. Sometimes this sounds like a Herculean task.

My summation was a long one. Since it was an especially important feature of this case, I quote from it at some length:

> Miss Harriman must prove her case by a fair preponderance of the evidence. And that means that the proof in behalf of the plaintiff must outweigh that of the defendant. So if you will, visualize before you the two scales of justice, or juror's scales: into the one scale place the believable evidence of the plaintiff, into the other that of the defendant. Weigh it. If the plaintiff's scale outweighs that of the defendant in the slightest degree, then the plaintiff has sustained the burden of proof. If the scales are evenly balanced, or if they tip in favor of the defendant, then the plaintiff has failed to sustain the burden of proof.
>
> But I think it is important that you understand that, this not being a criminal case, the proof need not be beyond a reasonable doubt. Some of you, since you are

now selected jointly between the Criminal Court as well
as Civil Court, may have, I don't know, either at this
experience or some previous experience, sat in a criminal
case where you know that the burden there is beyond
a reasonable doubt. But here the plaintiff in a civil case
has a lesser burden. It need not be beyond a reasonable
doubt. It need not be positively. It need only be by the
fair preponderance of the evidence.

I then set forth the central issues of the case as follows:

There are two main questions to be considered in this
case. First, Did the defendant, Dr. Deluca, in performing
the operation use reasonable care and diligence in the
exercise of his skill as a surgeon or was there a departure
from accepted proper method of performing the operation? In short, Was it done skillfully or carelessly? If, of
course, you are satisfied that it was done skillfully, that
is the end of the plaintiff's case. But if it was done carelessly, then the plaintiff is entitled to a verdict at your
hands.

There is a second part that the plaintiff must prove,
and that is, Was such departure or carelessness the proximate cause of the injuries or complications that developed?

I then proceeded to deal with the second issue, concerning
whether the hysterectomy caused the fistula—regardless of
the question as to whether or not the operation was performed
negligently:

I would like to address myself to the second question
first—namely, that of proximate cause. The proof is in
this case, although Miss Harriman tells you the leakage
as she remembers the wetness she felt occurred a few days

postoperative. That is her testimony. That is her recollection. But I submit to you it's of no great significance as
to what we finally know is a conceded fact—namely, that
eight days postoperatively, on June 25, 1959, there was
found by the doctor at the hospital, at least a determina-
tion was made, that there was clear fluid in the vagina
and a diagnosis made on that day or the next day of a
vesico-vaginal fistula.

Since there is no dispute now, and it is conceded that
eight days postoperative or nine days postoperative there
was a vesico-vaginal fistula found, and we now know
there is an abnormal opening in the bladder, the question
logically can be asked, What caused it? Whom do you
think we ought to ask? We are going to ask the doctor,
Dr. Deluca. You performed the operation. So at an examination-before-trial, which was held a year after this
operation, in June of 1960, as well as on the witness stand,
I asked Dr. Deluca that question. Since we have it in
the examination-before-trial, just very briefly I want to
read it to you. We are talking now, ladies and gentlemen,
about proximate cause—and this has nothing to do with
whether or not the hysterectomy was done carelessly or
skillfully. We are just considering the question, "Is there
any relationship between the fistula and the hysterectomy
he did?"

"Q. Could the hysterectomy you performed have
been the cause?
"A. I don't know."

Is the doctor being entirely frank with you? Is Dr.
Deluca being truthful when he says he doesn't know
whether or not this fistula which developed eight days
postoperative had any relationship to the hysterectomy
he performed? Just stop and think about that for a moment.

If there is any question about it, I want to show you, and you can take the hospital chart. You haven't had an opportunity to look at it, but it has been offered in evidence. When you get into the jury room, I want you to look at the summary sheet at Wittenborn Hospital, the hospital where the operation was performed, and there you will find the final diagnosis "myoma uteri." That is the operation for which she went in—namely, the reason why the hysterectomy was performed. "Secondary diagnosis or complication, *vesicle-vaginal fistula.*"

Is there any question in your mind? I am asking you, Is there any doubt in your mind that this vesico-vaginal fistula, which is diagnosed eight days postoperative, was related to the hysterectomy? Do you think for a moment that she had it before? Do you think that it just grew? Is that what you are supposed—what the defendant is trying to get you to believe? That we haven't established proximate cause? That this fistula had no relationship to the hysterectomy?

I'm sure that there is no one among you who has any doubt in his mind about the fact that this fistula was *proximately caused* by the hysterectomy.

I was now ready to argue the main point, that the hysterectomy had been negligently done:

In a courtroom things somehow have a way of getting out of focus. Questions are asked. There are objections. There are rulings by the court. And you folks sit silently by and witness what is going on. But if outside the atmosphere of the courtroom I were to discuss this problem in either your office or at your home, I might say to you: "You know, I have a client. She is fifty-two years of age. She went into a hospital for a hysterectomy." And you might ask, "Well, what kind was it?"

Then I would reply: "You know, the proof is that it was routine; that her uterus was only slightly enlarged; that in the course of the operation itself the doctor reports no special complications; that postoperative the microscopic and gross pathological reports indicate that there was no malignancy and that these fibroids or growths were small, and that eight days postoperative she developed an abnormal opening, a vesico-vaginal fistula. She started to leak urine."

Well, I am sure the first thing that would occur to you is, "What does the surgeon, the doctor who performed the operation, say about that?"

And I would say to you, "You know, we asked him that question. Let me read to you from the examination-before-trial, which was read to you and which his Honor instructed you is evidence in this case.

" 'Q. By vesicle-vaginal fistula, what is meant?
" 'A. It means an abnormal opening from her bladder into the vagina other than the usual opening.
" 'Q. An abnormal opening?
" 'A. Yes.
" 'Q. What caused it in this case?
" 'A. I don't know.' "

After hearing that you would probably say to me: "Well, that is odd. A surgeon doesn't know."

It might occur to you to say: "Well, after all, there are thousands of women—and hysterectomies are routine. This must have occurred in other situations. What does the medical literature say about it? What causes it? Somebody must know the answer if the surgeon who performed the operation doesn't know. Possibly the medical literature itself says so."

And I would then say to you: "You know, we did exactly that. We went to one of the outstanding medical authorities on the subject of vesicle-vaginal fistulas, Dr. Henry C. Falk, and we looked at his book, and by coincidence, the defendant, Dr. Deluca, recognizes Dr. Falk as one of the outstanding authorities, and in fact had suggested him as one of the doctors she should go to for the purpose of having this vesico-vaginal fistula repaired."

" 'What does Dr. Falk say in his textbook?' "

I would then say to you: "Well, Dr. Falk says that there are four causes for vesico-vaginal fistulas, and he lists them in his book. One is obstetrical trauma when there is difficult labor in the delivering of the child, in the movement of the child or a portion of it may pierce or injure the bladder. Two, radium or X ray given in excessive doses may cause a fistula to form. Three, malignancy, and finally, *surgical trauma.*"

Surgical trauma, of course, as we agreed, is surgical injury. We have established from the literature and very reluctantly got Dr. Deluca to admit that the major cause of vesico-vaginal fistulas is surgical injury.

Just stop and think of that for a moment. The *major* cause. Not an infrequent, not one of the small percentage of these causes that are given.

All right. Can it be prevented? Is that a fair question? When you are doing this operation, this hysterectomy, can this fistula be prevented?

What does Dr. Falk say to it? Let me just read to you what he has to say, because this was asked of Dr. Deluca: "Injury to the bladder in this region *can be avoided.*"

I was now prepared to make what I consider to be one of the strongest arguments that can be made to a jury. I was going to present a medical authority—recognized by the defendant—which supported our contention.

Now, ladies and gentleman, I don't know whether you

appreciate the significance of this. This textbook was not written for any lawsuit. It was not written for any court-room. This is written for medicine and science to be guided by. Dr. Falk not only gives you the four causes, but he tells you that injury *can be avoided*. He goes on to explain—and I asked Dr. Deluca about this—the *way* it can be avoided. You have got to get the bladder out of the operative site. It's as simple as that. And he points out that in the instances where surgical trauma occurred, the doctor just failed—was careless and didn't get it out of the operative site. So in the course of the operation a ligature, which is a tying-off, may have included the bladder, or in a suture that was put in the—what they call the anterior cuff of the vagina—when he comes to closing, may have included the bladder, and it should not include it. And so necrosis and sloughing develop. And in a week to three weeks later a fistula develops and you get, of course, the abnormal urine. Remember I asked the doctor about this?

I then dealt with my point that had the operation been done properly, a fistula should not have developed:

You and I know that there are no doubt hysterectomies performed on women where you are dealing with massive fibroids, where you are dealing with malignancy which may intertwine and enmesh the bladder itself, so that in the very course of the operation it just isn't possible— where the bladder is part of the operation. For that mat-ter, the intestines might be part of the operation itself because of the malignancy or these tremendous growths which exist in the bladder—in the uterus. That is not so in this case. And Dr. Blaise has said to you that if good, proper surgical procedure was performed this fistula should not have occurred, and he explained to you why and he explained to you the manner.

Now, it is true Dr. Blaise says, "I can't pinpoint exactly in which way it was that he injured this bladder." He mentioned at one point a clamp. It turns out the doctor didn't use a clamp. Then he said a ligature or tying-off, or in the suturing. Well, we know there was suturing, and we know there was tying-off. But Dr. Blaise says, no matter how it was done, *this result should not have occurred.*

Dr. Falk says it can be avoided. Dr. Blaise says so. Aside from Dr. Blaise, we have the literature which says it can be avoided.

And we have our own common sense. As I say, in a courtroom things get out of perspective. You know, when you ladies and gentlemen get into the jury box, that doesn't mean that your sense is to leave you, and what you know from your everyday knowledge and experience is to be ignored just because you are sitting in a courtroom as a juror. On the contrary, you should include that.

What does our common experience tell us? Some of us have had an operation. We have had relatives of ours submit to operations, and we know, for example, that if a person is having gallstones removed and in the course of the operation the doctor injures the liver or the pancreas, which are adjoining organs, our common sense tells us, unless there is some explanation for it, and there may be, and by the way there is no explanation for the fistula in this case. None. The answer is, "I don't know."

And so, too, if a child is having tonsils removed and in the course of the operation postoperative it develops that there has been an injury to the larynx, somebody would have a right to say, "Well, what happened?" Maybe there is an explanation. Or, if you, and many of you men may have had it, have had a prostate examination and the doctor in the course of maneuvering the tube punctures your colon and complications develop, maybe he's got an explanation for it, but you and I, our common sense would dictate that in normal experience that kind of result does not take place, because that kind of an injury should be avoided.

But, ladies and gentlemen, I am going to establish to you in one moment that if this hysterectomy had been done properly, a vesico-vaginal fistula should be avoided. I am going to prove it to you out of the mouth of Dr. Deluca himself. And I am reading again from the examination-before-trial which he gave. It is just one question and answer, and it is the heart of this case:

"Q. Doctor, we are agreed that if good procedure is adopted, good technique, that a vesico-vaginal fistula will not develop?

"A. *It ought not to.*"

Just stop and think about that for a minute. If good procedure and good technique are adopted, the vesico-vaginal fistula ought not to develop.

Now, ladies and gentlemen, if you remember nothing else of what I said to you this morning, I beg of you, remember that this is out of the mouth of the defendant himself.

My opponent had reiterated time and time again that it is undisputed that Dr. Deluca used the proper *technique* in doing the hysterectomy. But, I argued, this was not the issue:

Please don't be fooled by this argument that Dr. Deluca did use proper technique. I agree. We don't say, for example, that when he was performing the hysterectomy he used a technique for removing gallstones. We don't say that. He used the standard technique. But our criticism is in the *way* it was performed or executed.

I may know the ideal technique, for example, of how

to swing a golf club. I know to keep my head down, to bring my arm back straight, to pause on top, to follow through, and when I do that, when I follow that technique, of course, it is a good shot. But more times than not, because my execution isn't so good, the shot isn't so good.

And the same thing is true for you ladies and gentlemen who do cooking at home. You go to a cookbook, and it tells you how to make a particular dish. And you follow the cookbook as best you can—technique perfect, to the letter—but somehow it doesn't come out as nicely as you would like it.

Why? Not that there is anything wrong in your technique, but somehow in the performance or execution of it it was not precisely the way it should be done.

Now I came to the matter of the defense psychology of not admitting fault, because they had nothing to lose by saying, "I don't know"—hoping to create doubt in the jurors' minds:

I don't know how many of you have studied human nature or psychology. Even if you haven't studied psychology, just from your everyday experience as human beings, you know that when a person is blamed for something it's only natural that he would try to come up with some excuse for it. In other words, to try to get out from under.

And so, in this case Dr. Deluca and the defense figures, well, what have they got to lose? There is no point to admitting he was at fault. "We will come into court and we will say, 'I don't know.'"

Mind you, that is the defense. *No explanation.*

Dr. Eagan was called. Dr. Deluca was on the stand. Did you hear *any* explanation offered by any one of these men as to what caused this fistula? My adversary has raised some interesting questions as an advocate—and I can't cross-examine that. Remember when he opened to you only the other day? And even in his cross-examination of Dr. Blaise, he asked, "Doctor, don't different people heal differently?" The answer was "Yes."

But what does that mean? Don't people heal differently? Of course it is true! Some people heal better than others. But we are not dealing with the problem of healing here. It is not involved. And, as a matter of fact, insofar as the operation involving the uterus is concerned, she healed fine. There is nothing wrong with that part of the operation, and since the bladder *should not have been involved* there is no question involving the healing of the bladder because that was injured in the course of the operation.

Then for a while we heard something about *hemorrhage*. Did you hear Dr. Eagan or Dr. Deluca say that, in their opinion, hemorrhage had anything to do with this fistula which developed? There is not one word in the record—and I challenge the defendant to do that.

Then we come to the matter of *infection* that was injected into the case. All right. We know that for infection nobody could be blamed. When an operation is done, infection may develop over which the doctor may or may not have any control, but we will assume he is not to be blamed for an infection that develops. But has infection *anything* to do with this case?

Questioning of Dr. Eagan:

"Q. In your opinion, Doctor, what caused the vesicle-vaginal fistula in this case?
"A. I don't know. Infection."

That is the first time the word "infection" is injected into the case.

"Q. Doctor, was there any evidence of any infection?

"A. No, sir. Her temperature is very nice.

"Q. So that infection could be ruled out; is that correct?

"A. It could be ruled out."

Now, ladies and gentlemen, it is all right for my adversary—I have no quarrel with him. He is a lawyer. He is trying to do what he can to win a case in behalf of his client. It is all right for him as an argument to stand before you and try to muddy the waters with that kind of an argument. But you promised me, and you took your oath as a juror, that you would well and truly try this case on the evidence, and I submit to you that aside from the fact there is just no proof of any infection in this case —after all, the charts are here—that for any one of you to go out in the jury room and say, "Well, maybe it was infection," you would be doing this lady a gross injustice, particularly when we have now established otherwise. It would be different if there wasn't a word said about it, but the very surgeon who took care of her says to you, "Infection can be ruled out." Now my friend would like to rule it in. But I am sure that you ladies and gentlemen are not going to be fooled by that.

My opponent had raised the issue of a possible "error in judgment" on the doctor's part. There is a misunderstood concept that a doctor is not liable for a "mere error of judgment." That is incorrect. He is not liable for an "error in judgment" only if it is based on a *careful examination of all the facts.* In any event, I dealt with the subject as follows:

Then there is something injected about an error in judgment. Something new he just said. My adversary says that if he stitched and included the bladder, it is an error in judgment. Ladies and gentlemen, don't be fooled by that.

An error in judgment has to do with diagnosis. If a doctor is called in—a person complains, for example, of abdominal pains, and the doctor comes in and he palpates and he touches and he pokes around the stomach, and makes a diagnosis, "I think you have a stomach virus." Let's say it turns out to be appendicitis. That is an error in judgment for which the doctor may not be liable. Because in judging he has to make up his mind whether it is one condition or another.

Or, for example, another case of an error in judgment is, should a doctor operate or not. He has a patient before him and he says, "No, I think conservative therapy is indicated." And later on someone else second-guesses and says, "No, you should have operated."

Now you are dealing with judgment, what you should do.

We are dealing with an act here where we say, "You injured this bladder." There is no judgment any longer involved because we have established that good medical practice, skillful practice, requires that you get that bladder out of the field of operation so that you don't injure it with a ligature or with a needle.

My last point was to answer the claim that the complication of a vesico-vaginal fistula was one of the "hazards" of the surgery:

The last point I want to talk to you about concerns the assumption that a fistula is one of the "hazards" of hysterectomy. When Dr. Blaise was asked that question, he answered, "Yes." Look how misleading that could be. One of the hazards. A person gets onto an airplane. It is one of the hazards of being a passenger on a plane that it may crash. You get into an elevator. One of the hazards of being a passenger in an elevator is that it may crash. But what is the point of it? There are some risks that you assume. There are some hazards which are unavoidable and others which are avoidable. For example, if you have a blood transfusion, there is a hazard that you may develop hepatitis and, unfortunately, despite efforts that may have been made to purify the blood for the transfusion, it has been found that with the best of care hepatitis *cannot be prevented*—and it is one of the hazards in blood transfusion.

On the other hand, one of the *avoidable* hazards of a blood transfusion is that you may get mismatched blood: your type is "A," and they give you "B."

There are hazards and hazards. Some can be avoided, some cannot. And as Dr. Blaise said, sure there are hazhards; sure it is one of the hazards—but this is an *avoidable* hazard, and if the surgeon had performed this operation carefully and skillfully this lady's bladder would not have been injured.

Often, at the end of my summation I feel dissatisfied. I say to myself, "I should have said this" or "I should have said that." This time I was pleased. I thought I had carried conviction.

But I was wrong.

Following the court's instructions, as to the law, the jury retired. But after deliberating for many hours, they reported to the judge that they were deadlocked: they could not agree. As a result, the judge discharged the jury and set a new trial date.

I was sorely dismayed. In the many cases I had tried, I had never felt so confident of victory. I later spoke to some of the jurors, particularly those who had voted for the defendant, and they said that I had not proved that the doctor did anything wrong.

This did not seem possible. But when the case was scheduled for the second trial, I had renewed hopes that this time we would win. Unfortunately, the second trial never took place. Miss Harriman, timid and retiring as she was, had had her fill of court, and under no circumstances would she agree to appear at the trial. Ultimately, the case was settled for the nominal sum of $10,000.

I thought then, and I still think, that an injustice had been done to Miss Harriman. Jurors seem to require more proof in a malpractice case than they do in an ordinary accident case. Yet the law places no such burden on the plaintiff-patient.

It is perhaps fitting to end with the thought that some jurors probably place a protective mantle around the defendant doctor, fearful that a judgment against him might affect his standing in the community or his reputation among other doctors. Yet such is not the law, and in any event those are extraneous matters, no more relevant to the issue of justice than the fact that the plaintiff has been left penniless by the defendant's negligent treatment.

Did the plaintiff prove the negligence of the defendant? What do *you* think?

XI

"OF ALL THE ARTS,
THE MOST NOBLE"

Many instances of medical mal-
practice have been set forth in this book—stark cases, some
rife with blundering, ignorance, carelessness, and sheer negligence. You will remember vividly the doctor who failed to
terminate a cardiac catheterization when all the rules of good
medical practice, let alone practical common sense, suggested
that he do so; the doctor who operated on the wrong thigh of
a little girl who had been born with a dislocated hip; the slip
of a retractor that caused the cutting of a patient's sciatic
nerve; the cases involving improper use of anesthetics, wrong-
ful delay, careless use of the life-preserving and lethal scalpal.
You will remember the doctors who not only defaulted their
principal responsibility—"First, no harm to the patient"—
but who later compounded it by trying to cover up what
they had done. You will remember the "conspiracy of silence"
that leads some doctors into a false loyalty that demeans the
nobility of their calling.

The cases I have related are sad, tragic, and even frighten-
ing—and they are all true cases. People are maimed for life
because of some doctor's neglect of fundamental good medical practice—and people die, leaving bewildered and bereft

spouses and children who ask "Why? Why?" I might have
added dozens more cases from my own experience—and still
thousands more go unprosecuted every year.

But a warning is in order.

The world of medicine is not a house of horrors. You must
also remember that the cases I have presented are the exception and not the rule. There are many, many good, careful
doctors—doctors who save lives that might otherwise have
been lost. The vast majority of patients who receive medical
treatment *are* healed and not harmed.

Yes, despite all that has been said, despite all the slings and
arrows that have been cast, I, for one, still stand with Hippocrates's observation: "Medicine is, of all the Arts, the most
noble." Yet precisely because it is an "art" that deals with
human life and limb, precisely because such cases as I have
related have occurred, it is the more necessary that medicine
be practiced with the dedication of a *calling* and not that of
a business. What is needed is a reaffirmation of the doctor's
initial oath to "bring to the task a love of labor"; he should
remember that he has vowed, "With holiness I will . . . practice my Art."

Most important of all, this book will have served its purpose
if the life of just one patient is saved because someone who
read it learned from the mistakes of others.

GLOSSARY OF
PRINCIPAL LEGAL AND
MEDICAL TERMS

AFIBRINOGENEMIA — an abnormality of the blood-clotting mechanism usually caused by congenital absence of fibrinogen in the blood, and marked by a tendency to prolonged bleeding

ANGIOGRAM — a diagnostic procedure, employing contrast media, for X-raying blood vessels

AORTOGRAPHY — a diagnostic procedure performed by the injection of contrast media so that the aorta can be X-rayed

ARTERIOGRAM — a diagnostic procedure, employing contrast media, for X-raying the arteries

ARTHROPLASTY — repair of a joint

AUSTIN-MOORE PROSTHESIS — a metallic rounded head with a stem, used in major hip operations

BRONOCHOSCOPY — examination of the bronchi with the use of an examining instrument called the bronchoscope

CARDIAC CATHETERIZATION — a diagnostic procedure in which a long plastic tube, the catheter, is inserted into a vein and thence into the chambers of the heart

CAUDAL ANESTHESIA — a regional anesthesia that is frequently used in childbirth

CEREBRAL THROMBOSIS — clotting of the blood in the brain

CONTRAST MEDIA — a dye injected into a vein so that diagnostic X rays can be taken

CORONARY SCLEROSIS — hardening of the arteries of the heart

CROSS MATCHING — testing the donor's blood with that of the recipient to see if they are compatible.

"D AND C" — (dilation and curettage) a simple medical procedure used by gynecologists; scraping the womb

DAMAGES — the elements to be considered in arriving at fair and adequate compensation; namely, pain, suffering, disability, permanency, lost wages, hospital and doctor bills, and so forth

DELAYED FUNCTION TEST — a urological test to determine how well the kidney is putting out urine

DEVASCULARIZATION — lack of blood supply to tissues, with resultant damage to them

DIAGNOSTIC PROCEDURES — tests performed to aid the doctor in his diagnosis of a disease or ailment

DIODRAST — the name of a contrast medium that is injected into a vein so that an X ray can be taken

ESOPHAGOSCOPY — direct visual examination of the esophagus or gullet with an instrument called the esophagoscope

ETIOLOGIC — assigning or seeking to assign a cause

EXAMINATION-BEFORE-TRIAL — a legal procedure prior to the trial wherein a party or witness is questioned under oath by the opposing side

EXFOLIATE DERMATITIS — a particular type of skin disease; namely, separation of the skin in scales

FISTULA — an abnormal opening in an organ

FULMINATING LIVER NECROSIS — destruction of the liver

GI SERIES — gastrointestinal X rays by the use of a contrast medium such as barium

GASTROINTESTINAL SERIES — a diagnostic procedure, using contrast media, involving the digestive system (generally known as GI series)

HEMATOCRIT — an important blood test, showing the ratio of red blood cells in relationship to the volume of blood in the body

HEMORRHOIDECTOMY — operation for the removal of hemorrhoids

HEMOSTAT — a surgical instrument used to stop bleeding

HYDRONEPHROSIS — a collection of urine in the distended pelvis of the kidney, from obstructed outflow

HYSTERECTOMY — the removal of the womb or uterus

IVP — an intravenous pyelogram

INFORMED CONSENT — a legal doctrine that places a duty on the doctor to inform his patient of the risks connected with certain procedures so that the patient can decide whether to consent to it

INTRAVENOUS PYELOGRAM (IVP) — a diagnostic procedure involving the urinary system; a contrast media is employed

LATERAL X RAYS — X rays taken from the side

MALLEOLAR — hammerhead-shaped

MEDIASTINITIS — an inflammation of the mediostinum, which is located in the chest

OLECRANON — the "funny bone"; the large process of the ulna that projects behind the elbow joint

ORTHOPEDICS — the care and treatment of injuries and diseases involving bones and joints

PRIMA FACIE — evidence sufficient in law to raise a presumption of fact; literally, "on its face"

PROCTOSCOPE — an instrument used for a rectal examination

PROSTATECTOMY — surgical removal of the prostate gland

PROXIMATE CAUSE — the direct or immediate cause of a condition or event

REDUCING — an orthopedic process by which broken bones are brought back to their normal position

RES IPSA LOQUITUR — a legal term applied when something is said to be self-apparent; literally, "it speaks for itself"

RESPONDEAT SUPERIOR — the doctrine that employers are liable for certain acts of their employees

RETRACTOR — a surgical instrument used to hold open the lips of the wound

SAPHENOUS VEIN — either of the two chief superficial veins of the leg

SCIATIC NERVE — a nerve that originates in the lower spine and runs down the back of both legs

SIGMOIDOSCOPE — an instrument used for examining the lower end of the intestines

SPINAL BLOCK — the nerve block that is accomplished in spinal anesthesia

STATUTE OF LIMITATIONS — in medical malpractice cases, the time limit within which a patient may sue a doctor

SUBTROCHANTERIC OSTEOTOMY — removal of a piece of bone in an operation on a broken hip

TACHYCARDIA — a fast heartbeat

THYROIDECTOMY — an operation for the removal of the thyroid gland

TRANSPLANT — a portion of tissue used in grafting or transplanting

ULNAR NERVE — a nerve of the arm that controls the muscles of the hand

UREA NITROGEN TEST — a blood test to see how efficiently the kidneys are excreting wastes from the blood

URETER — one of two tubular organs through which urine flows from the kidneys to the bladder

URINE CULTURE — a test to determine if there is infection in the urine

VENTRICULAR FIBRILLATION — heart out of control

VITAL SIGNS — the blood pressure, pulse, and respiration

XYLOCAINE — a drug used for anesthetic purposes

70
71
72
74
75
76
77
79
81
83
85
86